*An Introduction to
the
Theory of Groups*

An Introduction to
the
Theory of Groups

GEORGE W. POLITES

Department of Mathematics
Illinois Wesleyan University

INTERNATIONAL TEXTBOOK COMPANY

Scranton, Pennsylvania

Preface

It is to be emphasized that this book is intended as an *introduction* to the theory of groups. It is hoped that a reading of this book will create a great deal of interest in the subject of groups, and that the reader will prolong this interest by continued reading in many of the fine books that go into the theory in much more depth. It is to be emphasized, too, that familiarity with and a knowledge of most of the material here is essential to a further study and understanding of the more advanced topics and specialized material on group theory.

The primary motive for the writing of the book was to provide a text for the study of groups by students engaged in independent study or honors work. It should also do very nicely for use in a special-topics course in mathematics, or in a mathematics seminar. It is directed mainly to the advanced undergraduate student and should provide enough material for a three-credit-hour course. The book also may have appeal for many graduate students as a reference, or as a supplement to a text in abstract algebra.

Finally, it should be stressed that most of the exercises in this book are of extreme importance and should be studied closely. Many results found later on in the text depend strongly on exercises that may occur much earlier. The examples also should be carefully noted, and the reader should try to construct others in addition to solving the ones given.

GEORGE W. POLITES

Bloomington, Illinois
June, 1968

Contents

1

Introduction

1-1. DEFINITION OF A GROUP

We begin by stating several definitions of a group and showing their equivalence. By a *mapping* of a set A into a set B we shall mean a rule which associates with each element a in A a unique element b in B. If f is a mapping from A into B, we shall indicate this by $f:A \to B$. If a is in A, $f(a)$ shall denote the element (image) in B that corresponds to a under the map f. By a binary operation on a set S we shall mean a mapping from $S \times S$ into S where $S \times S = \{(a, b);$ a and b are in S. (When we say that there is a binary operation defined on S, it is to be understood that S is a nonempty set.)

Definition 1 Let G be a set of elements and $*$ a binary operation defined on the elements of G. We call G a *group* with respect to $*$ if the following properties hold:

1. $(a*b)*c = a*(b*c)$ for all a, b, and c belonging to G. ($*$ is *associative*.)

2. There exists an element e belonging to G such that $a*e = e*a = a$ for every a in G. e is called an *identity*.

3. For each a belonging to G there exists an element y in G such that $a*y = y*a = e$. y is called an *inverse* of a.

Remark 1 It must be true in any group G that $a*b$ belongs to G whenever a and b belong to G. (G is *closed* with respect to $*$.)

Although a group is often defined as above, properties (2) and (3) need not say quite as much. Consider the following definition.

Definition 2 Let G be a set of elements and $*$ a binary operation defined on the elements of G. We call G a *group* with respect to $*$ if the following properties hold:

1. $(a*b)*c = a*(b*c)$ for all a, b, and c belonging to G.

2. There exists an element e belonging to G such that $e*a = a$ for every a

1

in G. e is called a *left identity*.

3. For each a belonging to G there exists an element y in G such that $y * a = e$. y is called a *left inverse* of a.

Remark 2   Parts (2) and (3) of Definition 2 may be referred to as "left" axioms. We could just as well have stated "right" axioms.

Note: We shall usually write ab for $a*b$ and refer to $*$ as "multiplication."

Theorem 1   Definition 1 is equivalent to Definition 2.

Proof: Clearly, Definition 1 implies Definition 2. Suppose G is defined by Definition 2. We must show that $ea = a$ implies $ae = a$, and $ya = e$ implies $ay = e$. Suppose $ya = e$. Now y belongs to G so there exists x in G such that $xy = e$. Thus $ay = e(ay) = (xy)(ay) = x(ya)y = x(ey) = xy = e$.   Therefore $ya = e$ implies $ay = e$.   Next, let a belong to G.   Then $a = ea = (ay)a = a(ya) = ae$, and $ea = a$ implies $ae = a$. Therefore Definition 2 implies Definition 1.

Definition 3   Let G be a set of elements and $*$ a binary operation defined on the elements of G. We call G a *group* with respect to $*$ if the following properties hold:

1. $(a*b)*c = a *(b*c)$ for all a, b, and c belonging to G.
2.   The equations $ax = b$ and $ya = b$ have solutions in G, where a and b are arbitrary elements of G.

Theorem 2   Definition 1 is equivalent to Definition 3.

Proof: Definition 1 implies Definition 3 since, if $ax = b$ and $ya = b$, we have $x = a^{-1}b$ belongs to G and $y = ba^{-1}$ belongs to G. Suppose G is defined by Definition 3. Let c belong to G and e denote a solution of the equation $xc = c$. Then $ec = c$. Consider the equation $cx = a$, a an arbitrary element in G. Then $ea = e(cx) = (ec)x = cx = a$. Therefore e is a left identity for G. Since the equation $xa = e$ is solvable in G for every a in G, each a has a *left inverse* in G. Thus Definition 2 is satisfied, and hence so is Definition 1 (Theorem 1).

Before discussing some examples of groups we note the following properties and definitions.

Theorem 3   The identity of a group is unique; the inverse of a group element is unique.

Proof: Suppose e and e' are identities for a group G. Then $e' = ee'$ (since e is an identity) $= e$ (since e' is an identity). Suppose y and y' are inverses of the group element a. Then $y = ye = y(ay') = (ya)y' = ey' = y'$.

Note: We shall usually write a^{-1} for the inverse of a (or $-a$ if the operation is "addition").

Theorem 4 Let G be a group and a and b belong to G. Then $(ab)^{-1} = b^{-1}a^{-1}$ and $(a^{-1})^{-1} = a$.

Proof: $(b^{-1}a^{-1})(ab) = b^{-1}(a^{-1}a)b = b^{-1}eb = b^{-1}b = e$, which implies $b^{-1}a^{-1} = (ab)^{-1}$. $a(a^{-1}) = e$ implies $a = (a^{-1})^{-1}$.

Definition 4 Let G be a group and a belong to G. We define $a^1 = a$, $a^2 = aa$, and, in general, if k is a positive integer such that a^k has been defined, we define $a^{k+1} = a^k a$. We define $a^0 = e$ and $a^{-k} = (a^{-1})^k$.

Note: Since $e = e^k = (aa^{-1})^k = a^k(a^{-1})^k$, ($a$ and a^{-1} commute), we see that $(a^{-1})^k$ is the inverse of a^k. Thus $(a^k)^{-1} = (a^{-1})^k = a^{-k}$. The reader should verify that $a^m a^n = a^{m+n}$ and $(a^m)^n = a^{mn}$ hold in a group.

Definition 5 If $ab = ba$ for all a and b belonging to G, a group, we call G an *Abelian* (commutative) group.

We now give several examples of groups.

Example 1 The integers with respect to addition, the rationals (or reals) with respect to addition, the nonzero rationals (or reals) with respect to multiplication, and the complex numbers with respect to addition, are all examples of Abelian groups.

Example 2 The set of all nonsingular n by n matrices and the set of all orthogonal n by n matrices are groups with respect to matrix multiplication.

Example 3 Consider the symmetries of the square (Fig. 1). These are R, a 90°

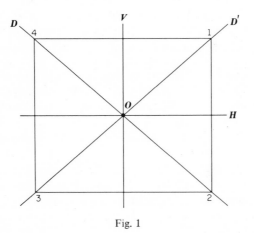

Fig. 1

rotation clockwise around its center O; R' and R'', similar rotations through 180° and 270°; I, a rotation about O of 360°; H a reflection in the horizontal axis through O; V a reflection in the vertical axis through O; D and D', reflections in the diagonals.

We define a binary operation $*$ on these symmetries as follows: $X * Y$ shall be the symmetry which achieves the same rearrangement of the square as is obtained by first performing Y and then X. Table 1 is an example of a $*$ table (usu-

TABLE 1

$*$	I	R	R'	R''	H	V	D	D'
I	I	R	R'	R''	H	V	D	D'
R	R	R'	R''	I	D	D'	V	H
R'	R'	R''	I	R	V	H	D'	D
R''	R''	I	R	R'	D'	D	H	V
H	H	D'	V	D	I	R'	R''	R
V	V	D	H	D'	R'	I	R	R''
D	D	H	D'	V	R''	R''	I	R'
D'	D'	V	D	H	R''	R	R'	I

ally called a multiplication table, or a Cayley table). $H*R$, for example, is the entry in the row designated by H and the column headed by R. Thus $HR = D'$.

Inspection of the table indeed shows that $*$ is binary, that I is the identity, and that each element has an inverse. The associative property follows from the fact that $(XY)Z$ and $X(YZ)$ is in each case the symmetry obtained by first performing Z and then Y and then X. Thus the symmetries of the square form a group with respect to $*$. It is clear, however, that it is not Abelian.

Remark 3   We may of course consider the symmetries of any regular polygon of $n \geqslant 3$ sides and see that in each case we obtain a non-Abelian group with respect to a binary operation $*$ defined as in Example 3. (How many symmetries are there corresponding to a fixed n?)

Example 4   Suppose S is a set containing n elements and denote by S_n the set of all 1-1 mappings of S onto S. Such a mapping is called a *permutation* of S. [Suppose f is a mapping from A to B and x and y belong to A. If $f(x) = f(y)$ implies that $x = y$, then f is said to be a *one to one* (1-1) mapping. If b is an arbitrary element of B and there is an a in A such that $f(a) = b$, we say that f is a mapping from A onto B.]   For f and g in S_n we define $f*g$ as follows: $(f*g)(x) = f(g(x))$, for all x in S. It is left to the reader to verify that S_n, together with $*$, is a group. (S_n is called the *symmetric group* on n symbols.)

Remark 4   One could discuss the set of 1-1 mappings of an infinite set S onto itself, with $*$ defined as above, and still obtain a group.

Example 5   As a special case of Example 4 we consider the following. Suppose S is a set containing four elements, which we denote by 1, 2, 3, 4. Then S_4 will consist of 24 permutations as shown.

$$P_1 = \begin{pmatrix} 1\ 2\ 3\ 4 \\ 1\ 2\ 3\ 4 \end{pmatrix} \quad P_7 = \begin{pmatrix} 1\ 2\ 3\ 4 \\ 1\ 3\ 4\ 2 \end{pmatrix} \quad P_{13} = \begin{pmatrix} 1\ 2\ 3\ 4 \\ 4\ 2\ 3\ 1 \end{pmatrix} \quad P_{19} = \begin{pmatrix} 1\ 2\ 3\ 4 \\ 4\ 1\ 2\ 3 \end{pmatrix}$$

$$P_2 = \begin{pmatrix} 1\ 2\ 3\ 4 \\ 2\ 1\ 4\ 3 \end{pmatrix} \quad P_8 = \begin{pmatrix} 1\ 2\ 3\ 4 \\ 1\ 4\ 2\ 3 \end{pmatrix} \quad P_{14} = \begin{pmatrix} 1\ 2\ 3\ 4 \\ 3\ 1\ 4\ 2 \end{pmatrix} \quad P_{20} = \begin{pmatrix} 1\ 2\ 3\ 4 \\ 3\ 4\ 2\ 1 \end{pmatrix}$$

$$P_3 = \begin{pmatrix} 1\ 2\ 3\ 4 \\ 3\ 4\ 1\ 2 \end{pmatrix} \quad P_9 = \begin{pmatrix} 1\ 2\ 3\ 4 \\ 3\ 2\ 4\ 1 \end{pmatrix} \quad P_{15} = \begin{pmatrix} 1\ 2\ 3\ 4 \\ 2\ 4\ 1\ 3 \end{pmatrix} \quad P_{21} = \begin{pmatrix} 1\ 2\ 3\ 4 \\ 1\ 2\ 4\ 3 \end{pmatrix}$$

$$P_4 = \begin{pmatrix} 1\ 2\ 3\ 4 \\ 4\ 3\ 2\ 1 \end{pmatrix} \quad P_{10} = \begin{pmatrix} 1\ 2\ 3\ 4 \\ 4\ 2\ 1\ 3 \end{pmatrix} \quad P_{16} = \begin{pmatrix} 1\ 2\ 3\ 4 \\ 1\ 3\ 2\ 4 \end{pmatrix} \quad P_{22} = \begin{pmatrix} 1\ 2\ 3\ 4 \\ 3\ 2\ 1\ 4 \end{pmatrix}$$

$$P_5 = \begin{pmatrix} 1\ 2\ 3\ 4 \\ 2\ 3\ 1\ 4 \end{pmatrix} \quad P_{11} = \begin{pmatrix} 1\ 2\ 3\ 4 \\ 2\ 4\ 3\ 1 \end{pmatrix} \quad P_{17} = \begin{pmatrix} 1\ 2\ 3\ 4 \\ 4\ 3\ 1\ 2 \end{pmatrix} \quad P_{23} = \begin{pmatrix} 1\ 2\ 3\ 4 \\ 1\ 4\ 3\ 2 \end{pmatrix}$$

$$P_6 = \begin{pmatrix} 1\ 2\ 3\ 4 \\ 3\ 1\ 2\ 4 \end{pmatrix} \quad P_{12} = \begin{pmatrix} 1\ 2\ 3\ 4 \\ 4\ 1\ 3\ 2 \end{pmatrix} \quad P_{18} = \begin{pmatrix} 1\ 2\ 3\ 4 \\ 2\ 3\ 4\ 1 \end{pmatrix} \quad P_{24} = \begin{pmatrix} 1\ 2\ 3\ 4 \\ 2\ 1\ 3\ 4 \end{pmatrix}$$

Here we are using a convenient notation to represent the 1-1 mappings of S onto S. P_9, for example, is the map which sends 1 onto 3, 2 onto 2, 3 onto 4, and 4 onto 1. It is to be remembered that in performing the operation $*$ on the elements of S_4, we first perform the map on the right, then the one on the left. As an example, $P_3 * P_9 = P_8$.

Table 2 is a partial (for obvious reasons) multiplication table for S_4. Clearly, S_4 is non-Abelian.

TABLE 2

	P_1	P_2	P_3	P_4	P_5	P_6	P_7	P_8	P_9	P_{10}	P_{11}	P_{12}	$\ldots P_{24}$
P_1	P_1	P_2	P_3	P_4	P_5	P_6	P_7	P_8	P_9	P_{10}	P_{11}	P_{12}	
P_2	P_2	P_1	P_4	P_3	P_8	P_{10}	P_{11}	P_5	P_{12}	P_6	P_7	P_9	
P_3	P_3	P_4	P_1	P_2	P_{12}	P_7	P_6	P_9	P_8	P_{11}	P_{10}	P_5	
P_4	P_4	P_3	P_2	P_1	P_9	P_{11}	P_{10}	P_{12}	P_5	P_7	P_6	P_8	
P_5	P_5	P_9	P_8	P_{12}	P_6	P_1	P_2	P_{11}	P_7	P_4	P_3	P_{10}	
P_6	P_6	P_7	P_{11}	P_{10}	P_1	P_5	P_9	P_3	P_2	P_{12}	P_8	P_4	
P_7	P_7	P_6	P_{10}	P_{11}	P_3	P_{12}	P_8	P_1	P_4	P_5	P_9	P_2	
P_8	P_8	P_{12}	P_5	P_9	P_{10}	P_2	P_1	P_7	P_{11}	P_3	P_4	P_6	
P_9	P_9	P_5	P_{12}	P_8	P_{11}	P_4	P_3	P_6	P_{10}	P_1	P_2	P_7	
P_{10}	P_{10}	P_{11}	P_7	P_6	P_2	P_8	P_{12}	P_4	P_1	P_9	P_5	P_3	
P_{11}	P_{11}	P_{10}	P_6	P_7	P_4	P_9	P_5	P_2	P_3	P_8	P_{12}	P_1	
P_{12}	P_{12}	P_8	P_9	P_5	P_7	P_3	P_4	P_{10}	P_6	P_2	P_1	P_{11}	
.													
.													
.													
P_{24}													

Remark 5 S_n for $n \geqslant 3$ is non-Abelian.

Proof: Let x_1, x_2, and x_3 be distinct elements in S and define the mappings f and g as follows: $f(x_1) = x_2, f(x_2) = x_3, f(x_3) = x_1, f(y) = y$ for any y in S other than x_1, x_2, or x_3 $g(x_1) = x_1, g(x_2) = x_3, g(x_3) = x_2, g(y) = y$ for any y in S other than x_2 or x_3. Clearly, f and g belong to S_n. Now $(fg)(x_1) = f(g(x_1))$ $= f(x_1) = x_2$, while $(gf)(x_1) = g(f(x_1)) = g(x_2) = x_3$.

Exercise 1   Prove that if $x^2 = e$ for every x in G, a group, then G is Abelian.

1-2.   SUBGROUPS
AND
COSETS

It may well be the case that a group contains a subset that meets all the requirements to itself be a group. Clearly, $\{e\}$ is one such subset. This leads to the following definition.

Definition 6   A subset H of a group G is a *subgroup* of G, if H is itself a group relative to the binary operation defined in G.

Actually, one need not explicitly show that every property (as stated, say, in Definition 1) is satisfied by a subset H of a group G in order to show it is a subgroup. This is the content of our next theorem (and remark).

Theorem 5   A subset H of a group G is a subgroup of G if, and only if, the following hold:

   (i)   if a and b belong to H, then ab belongs to H.
   (ii)   if h belongs to H, then h^{-1} belongs to H.

Proof: Clearly, if H is a subgroup of G, then (i) and (ii) hold. Conversely, suppose H is a subset of G such that a and b in H imply ab in H, and h in H implies h^{-1} in H. Now h and h^{-1} in H imply $hh^{-1} = e$ in H (by (i)). Since $*$ is associative on G, it is associative on H. Therefore H is a group.

Remark 6   (i) and (ii) above are equivalent to: (iii) if a and b are in H then ab^{-1} is in H.

Proof: Clearly, (i) and (ii) imply (iii). Suppose (iii) holds and that a and b belong to H. a in H implies $aa^{-1} = e$ in H (by (iii)), and so $eb^{-1} = b^{-1}$ belongs to H. Thus (iii) implies (ii). Furthermore, $a(b^{-1})^{-1} = ab$ belongs to H. Thus (iii) implies (i).

Exercise 2   Suppose H and K are subgroups of a group G. Prove that $H \cap K$ is also a subgroup of G. ($H \cap K$ denotes the set of elements common to both H and K.)

Definition 7   Let G be a group and H a subgroup of G. The set $Ha = \{ha; h$ in H, a in G, a fixed$\}$ is called a *right coset* of H. (A left coset aH may be defined similarly.)

   Note: If the operation in G is "addition," then the set $H + a = \{h + a;$ h in H, a in G, a fixed$\}$ would be a right coset of H.

Remark 7   Since $He = H = eH$, we see that H is itself a right (left) coset of H. Also, since e belongs to H, we have that a belongs to Ha (aH). Thus every element of G is in some right (left) coset of H. We may regard a as the representative of Ha (aH).

Theorem 6   If $Ha \cap Hb \neq \phi$, then $Ha = Hb$. (ϕ denotes the empty set.)

   Proof: Suppose x belongs to $Ha \cap Hb$. Then we may write $x = h_1 a$ and $x = h_2 b$ where h_1 and h_2 belong to H. Thus $h_1 a = h_2 b$ and so $a = h_1^{-1} h_2 b$. Therefore $ha = h(h_1^{-1} h_2 b) = h_3 b$ where $h_3 = h h_1^{-1} h_2$ belongs to H. Thus $Ha \subseteq Hb$. Similarly one shows $Hb \subseteq Ha$. (We shall write $A \subseteq B$ or $B \supseteq A$ to indicate that A is a *subset* of B. If A is a subset of B, but $\neq B$, we shall write $A \subset B$ or $B \supset A$ and call A a *proper subset* of B.)

Remark 8   The number of elements in any right (left) coset of H is the same as the number in H. We also note that $(Ha)^{-1} = a^{-1}H$ and $(bH)^{-1} = Hb^{-1}$. ($(Ha)^{-1}$ is the set consisting of the inverses of all elements in the coset Ha.) Thus there is a 1-1 correspondence between right and left cosets of H.

Exercise 3   Prove that $(Ha)^{-1} = a^{-1}H$.

   To illustrate the concepts of subgroup and coset we consider the following examples.

Example 6   The subsets $K_1 = \{I, H\}$ and $K_2 = \{I, R, R', R''\}$ of the group of symmetries of the square (Example 3) are also subgroups. The right cosets of K_1 are the sets $\{I, H\}$, $\{R, D'\}$, $\{R', V\}$, and $\{R'', D\}$, while the left cosets of K_1 are $\{I, H\}$, $\{R, D\}$, $\{R', V\}$, and $\{R'', D'\}$. The right cosets of K_2 are the sets $\{I, R, R', R''\}$ and $\{H, D, V, D'\}$. These are also the left cosets of K_2. It is to be noted that it is not always the case that the collection of right cosets of a subgroup is the same as the collection of left cosets.

Example 7   Suppose G is the group of integers with respect to addition and H the subgroup of G consisting of all multiples of 4. (The reader should show that H is a subgroup.) Then the right cosets of H are the sets $H, H + 1, H + 2$, and $H + 3$ (see note following Definition 7). Clearly, these are also the left cosets of H.

   Note: In the above example, we may of course consider the subset consisting of all multiples of any fixed integer n.

Definition 8   The *order* of a group G is the number of elements in G. A *finite group* is a group of finite order. A group has infinite order if it does not have finite order.

Remark 9   Since each element of G is in some right coset of H, we write $G = H + Hx_2 + Hx_3 + \cdots$ to indicate that the cosets $H, Hx_2, Hx_3, \ldots$ are disjoint and exhaust G. (We take $x_1 = e$.) If the number of distinct right cosets of H in G is r, then we have $G = H + Hx_2 + \cdots + Hx_r$.

Definition 9   The number r of distinct right (left) cosets of a subgroup H in a group G is called the *index* of H in G and is denoted by $[G:H]$.
   Note: Since we may take $H = \{e\}$, we see that the order of G may be defined as the index of the identity subgroup.

Exercise 4   In a group of order $2n$, n a positive integer, prove there exists an element besides e which is its own inverse.
   We now prove one of the most important theorems of group theory.

Theorem 7   (Lagrange) If G is a group of order n, the order of every subgroup H of G is a divisor of n.
   Proof: Suppose H has order t. We decompose G according to right cosets of H obtaining $G = H + Hx_2 + Hx_3 + \cdots + Hx_r$. Now each coset Hx_i contains t elements. Since these cosets are disjoint we have $n = rt$.
   Note: The order of a group G is the product of the order of a subgroup H and the index of H in G.

Theorem 8   Suppose G is a group, H a subgroup of G, and K a subgroup of H. Then $[G:K] = [G:H]\,[H:K]$.
   Proof: This is immediate from Lagrange's Theorem.

1-3.   CYCLIC GROUPS

   Of special interest are the so-called cyclic groups. We introduce them here.

Definition 10   If a group G contains an element a such that every element of G is of the form a^k for some integer k (or of the form ka if the operation is $+$), we say that G is a *cyclic group*. a is called a *generator* of G.
   We distinguish two cases:
   1.   All powers a^k are distinct. Then the cyclic group $G = \{\cdots, a^{-2}, a^{-1}, a^0, a, a^2, \cdots\}$ is infinite.
   2. $a^h = a^k$, $h > k$. Here $a^{h-k} = e$ $(h - k > 0)$. Let m be the smallest posi-

tive exponent for which $a^m = e$. Then a^0, a, a^2, $\cdots$, a^{m-1} are all distinct. For suppose $a^t = a^s$ ($0 \leqslant s < t \leqslant m-1$). Then $a^{t-s} = e$ ($0 < t - s < m$), which contradicts the assumption made on m. Now every integer n can be written in the form $n = qm + r$, $0 \leqslant r < m$ (division algorithm). Thus $a^n = a^{qm+r} = a^{qm} \cdot a^r = ea^r = a^r$. Therefore we see that all powers of a are contained in the sequence a^0, a, a^2, ..., a^{m-1} and so $G = \{a^0, a, a^2, \ldots, a^{m-1}\}$ is a cyclic group of order m.

Remark 10 If G is a group and a belongs to G, the set $H = \{a^k ; k$ an integer$\}$ is a subgroup of G. Thus every element of a group generates a cyclic subgroup.

Definition 11 The order of the cyclic group generated by a is called the *order* of the element a. a is an element of infinite order if all powers of a are distinct.

The following are immediate consequences of Lagrange's Theorem.

1. If G is a finite group, the order of each element of G is a divisor of the order of G.

2. A group of order p, p a prime, is a cyclic group. Every element $\neq e$ is a generator.

3. If G has order n, then $a^n = e$ for every a in G.

Proof of (3): Suppose a belongs to G and the order of a is m. Then $mk = n$. Now $a^m = e$. Thus $a^n = a^{mk} = (a^m)^k = e$.

Note: Every cyclic group is Abelian since $a^i a^j = a^{i+j} = a^{j+i} = a^j a^i$, for arbitrary integers i and j.

The following are examples of cyclic groups.

Example 8 The integers under addition are generated by 1.

Example 9 Let $G = \{1, -1, i, -i\}$ and $*$ be the usual multiplication for complex numbers. i and $-i$ both generate G. ($i = \sqrt{-1}$, so $i^2 = -1$.)

Example 10 The group K_2 (see Example 6) is generated by R. (Is this the only generator?)

Example 11 Consider the fixed positive integer 11, and let a and b be any integers. We say that *a is congruent to b modulo* 11 (for this we will write $a \equiv b$ (mod 11)) if $a - b$ is divisible by 11. For example, $27 \equiv 5$ (mod 11) since $27 - 5$ is divisible by 11. One easily shows that every integer is congruent (mod 11) to exactly one of the integers 0, 1, 2, ..., 10. Now let $G = \{1, 2, \ldots, 10\}$ and define an operation $*$ on G as follows: for a and b in G, $a*b$ is the ordinary product of a and b "reduced" modulo 11. For example, $3*9 = 5$ (since $3 \cdot 9 = 27 \equiv 5$ (mod 11)). The complete $*$ table for G is given in Table 3. Inspection of the table shows G to be an Abelian group with respect to $*$. Now G is also cyclic, since 2 is a generator.

TABLE 3

	1	2	3	4	5	6	7	8	9	10
1	1	2	3	4	5	6	7	8	9	10
2	2	4	6	8	10	1	3	5	7	9
3	3	6	9	1	4	7	10	2	5	8
4	4	8	1	5	9	2	6	10	3	7
5	5	10	4	9	3	8	2	7	1	6
6	6	1	7	2	8	3	9	4	10	5
7	7	3	10	6	2	9	5	1	8	4
8	8	5	2	10	7	4	1	9	6	3
9	9	7	5	3	1	10	8	6	4	2
10	10	9	8	7	6	5	4	3	2	1

Exercise 5   Generalize Example 11 by replacing the fixed positive integer 11 by any positive integer $m > 1$. Under what conditions will the set $G = \{1, 2, \ldots, m - 1\}$ be a cyclic group?

Remark 11   It is to be noted that for any fixed positive integer m, the set $G = \{0, 1, 2, \ldots, m - 1\}$ is always a group (in fact, cyclic) if the binary operation $*$ defined on G is as follows: $a * b$ is the ordinary sum of a and b "reduced" modulo m. Henceforth, a group of this type will be referred to as the *additive group of integers modulo m* and shall be denoted by $I/(m)$.

One can observe that all subgroups of the cyclic groups described in the above examples are also cyclic. That this is the case in any cyclic group is our next theorem.

Theorem 9   A subgroup H of a cyclic group G is itself cyclic.

Proof: Suppose G is generated by a and let m be the smallest positive integer such that a^m is in H. (We assume $H \neq \{e\}$.) Now $H \subset G$; thus any element of H is of the form a^k for some integer k. Using the division algorithm, we may write $k = qm + r$ $(0 \leqslant r < m)$. Thus $a^k = a^{qm+r} = (a^m)^q \cdot a^r$, which implies $a^r = (a^m)^{-q} a^k$. Now a^m belongs to H and a^k belongs to H. Therefore a^r is in H. Hence $r = 0$ and $k = qm$. Therefore every element of H has the form $a^{qm} = (a^m)^q$. Thus H is cyclic generated by a^m.

Remark 12   In Theorem 9, suppose G has order n. Then $a^n = e$ belongs to H and $n = qm$. Thus every subgroup H of G is generated by an element of the form a^m where m divides n. Conversely, if the order of G is $n = mq$, $H = \{a^0, a^q, a^{2q}, \ldots, a^{(m-1)q}\}$ is a cyclic subgroup of G having order m. Thus we see the existence of a subgroup of G having order m for any divisor m of the order of G.

Theorem 10   Let G be a group, $G \neq \{e\}$. Then G has no proper subgroups if, and only if, G is a finite cyclic group of prime order.

Proof: The "if" part is immediate from Lagrange's Theorem. To prove "only if," let $x \neq e$ belong to G. Then the cyclic group generated by x is all of G. If x has infinite order then x^2 generates a proper subgroup. Thus x must have finite order n. If $n = rs$, $r > 1$, $s > 1$, then x^r generates a proper subgroup of order s. Therefore n must be a prime.

Exercise 6   Suppose G is an Abelian group. Let a and b belong to G such that the order of a is r and the order of b is s, where r and s are relatively prime. Show that ab has order rs. (Two integers n and m are *relatively prime* if their only common factors are 1 and – 1. We write $(n,m) = 1$ to indicate that n and m are relatively prime.)

Exercise 7   Suppose G is cyclic of order n with generator a. Show that a^k is also a generator of G if, and only if, k and n are relatively prime.

Remark 13   Suppose n is a positive integer and denote by $\phi(n)$ the number of positive integers less than n that are relatively prime to n. (ϕ is known as the *Euler ϕ function*.) Then Exercise 7 says that the number of generators for a cyclic group of order n is $\phi(n)$. In particular, the number of generators for the group of Example 11 is $\phi(10) = 4$. (Since 2 is a generator, so are $3 \cdot 2$, $7 \cdot 2$, and $9 \cdot 2$, by Exercise 7.)

Exercise 8   Suppose G is an Abelian group of order 6 containing an element of order 3. Prove G is cyclic.

Exercise 9   Show that the elements of finite order in any commutative group G form a subgroup.

Exercise 10   Prove that a group of order p^m, p a prime, must contain a subgroup of order p. (Groups of this type are of great interest and will be discussed in Chapter 3.)

Exercise 11   Suppose G has only one element (say a) of order 2. Show $xa = ax$ for all x in G.

Exercise 12   Prove that every non-Abelian group contains proper subgroups.

1-4.   ISOMORPHISMS

Of prime importance in mathematics is the concept of isomorphism. We define it here for groups.

Definition 12   Let G and G' be groups with respect to $*$ and $*'$ respectively. We say that G is *isomorphic* to G' if there exists a 1-1 mapping π of G onto G' such that if $\pi(a) = a'$ and $\pi(b) = b'$, then $\pi(a*b) = a'*'b'$. The mapping π is called an *isomorphism* of G onto G'.

Example 12 Consider the set $G' = \{1,3,5,7\}$ and the operation $*'$ defined on G' to be ordinary multiplication "reduced" modulo 8. One easily verifies that

TABLE 4

	1	3	5	7
1	1	3	5	7
3	3	1	7	5
5	5	7	1	3
7	7	5	3	1

G' together with $*'$ is a group (see Table 4). Table 5 is the $*$ table for the subset $K_3 = \{I,H,V,R'\}$ of the group of symmetries of the square (Example 3).

TABLE 5

	I	H	V	R'
I	I	H	V	R'
H	H	I	R'	V
V	V	R'	I	H
R'	R'	V	H	I

That K_3 is a group (subgroup of the group of symmetries of the square) follows from Theorem 5.

Now consider the mapping $\pi : K_3 \to G'$ defined by $\pi(I) = 1$, $\pi(H) = 3$, $\pi(V) = 5$, and $\pi(R') = 7$. Clearly, π is 1-1 and onto. That $\pi(a*b) = \pi(a) *' \pi(b)$ for arbitrary elements a and b in K_3, is easily verified. Thus the groups K_3 and G' are isomorphic and π is an isomorphism. (Is π the only isomorphism of K_3 onto G'?)

Example 13 The mapping $x \to \log x$ is an isomorphism of the group G of positive real numbers under multiplication onto the group G' of all real numbers under addition.

Exercise 13 Prove that if π is an isomorphism of a group G onto a group G', then: (i) $\pi(e) = e'$ (e is the identity of G, e' the identity of G'); (ii) $\pi(a) = a'$ implies $\pi(a^{-1}) = (a')^{-1}$.

Exercise 14 Show that the group of Example 3 is isomorphic to a subgroup of the group S_4. (See Example 5.) Generalize this to the group of symmetries of any regular polygon and the groups S_n.

Remark 14 With some thought, one should realize that isomorphic groups have the same structure. Essentially, the only difference is the notation used to describe the elements and the nature of the operations defined on these elements.

Our next theorem completely characterizes the cyclic groups.

Theorem 11   (i) Every cyclic group G of infinite order is isomorphic to the additive group I of integers; (ii) Every cyclic group G of order n is isomorphic to the additive group $I/(n)$ of integers modulo n. (See Remark 11.)

Proof: For (i), define $\pi:G \to I$ by $\pi(a^k) = k$, where a is a generator of G. For (ii), define $\pi:G \to I/(n)$ by $\pi(a^k) = k$, where a is a generator of G and k is reduced modulo n.

We have seen that many groups may be regarded as permutation groups; that is, as groups whose elements are permutations (Exercise 14). It is somewhat remarkable that this is true for any group. We prove this now.

Theorem 12   (Cayley) Every group G is isomorphic to a permutation group.

Proof: Let a be a fixed element of G and consider the mapping $\pi_a:G \to G$ defined by $\pi_a(x) = ax$. π_a is onto, since for y in G we have $\pi_a(a^{-1}y) = y$. Clearly, π_a is 1-1. Thus π_a is a permutation of G for each a. Let P be the set consisting of the mappings π_a. Since $\pi_b^{-1} = \pi_b^{-1}$ (why?) we have, for π_a and π_b belonging to P, $(\pi_a\pi_b^{-1})(x) = \pi_a(\pi_b^{-1}(x)) = \pi_a(b^{-1}x) = a(b^{-1}x) = (ab^{-1})x = \pi_{ab}^{-1}(x)$, which implies that P is a group (Remark 6). Now consider the mapping $\varphi:G \to P$ defined by $\varphi(a) = \pi_a$. If $\pi_a = \pi_b$ (that is, $\pi_a(x) = \pi_b(x)$ for all x in G), then $ax = bx$, which implies that $a = b$ and φ is 1-1. Since $\varphi(ab) = \pi_{ab} = \pi_a\pi_b = \varphi(a)\varphi(b)$, φ is an isomorphism. This concludes the proof.

1-5.   NORMAL SUBGROUPS

In this section we shall introduce what is perhaps the most important type of subgroup of a group. We begin with the following theorem.

Theorem 13   Let H be a subgroup of G and x belong to G. Then $K = x^{-1}Hx = \{x^{-1}hx; h \text{ in } H\}$ is a subgroup of G.

Proof: Let $x^{-1}h_1x$ and $x^{-1}h_2x$ belong to K. We will show that $(x^{-1}h_1x) \times (x^{-1}h_2x)^{-1}$ belongs to K (see Remark 6). Now $(x^{-1}h_1x)(x^{-1}h_2x)^{-1} = (x^{-1}h_1x) \times (x^{-1}h_2^{-1}x) = x^{-1}h_1(xx^{-1})h_2^{-1}x = x^{-1}h_1h_2^{-1}x = x^{-1}h_3x$, which is an element of K (where $h_3 = h_1h_2^{-1}$ is in H).

Definition 13   If $G = \{x_1, x_2, \dots\}$ is a group and H is a subgroup of G, the subgroups $x_1^{-1}Hx_1, x_2^{-1}Hx_2, \cdots$ are called *conjugates* of H. (We shall also refer to the sets $x_1^{-1}Hx_1, x_2^{-1}Hx_2, \dots$ as conjugates of H when H is any *subset* of G. Of particular interest are the conjugates of a single element, which we discuss in a later section.)

Note: Since e belongs to G, $e^{-1}He = H$ is a conjugate of H.

Definition 14 If in Definition 13 we have $H = x_1^{-1}Hx_1 = x_2^{-1}Hx_2 = \cdots$, we call H a *normal* (self-conjugate, invariant) *subgroup* of G. Thus H is a normal subgroup of G if $x^{-1}Hx = H$ for all x belonging to G. We write $H \triangle G$ to denote H is a normal subgroup of G.

Remark 15 Suppose $x^{-1}Hx \subseteq H$ for all x in G. Then $x^{-1}hx$ belongs to H for all x in G and h in H. If k belongs to H, then $xkx^{-1} = h$ also belongs to H. Thus $k = x^{-1}hx$ is in $x^{-1}Hx$ and we have $H \subseteq x^{-1}Hx$. Hence $H = x^{-1}Hx$ for all x in G, and so $H \triangle G$. Therefore, to show H is a normal subgroup of G, we need only show $x^{-1}Hx \subseteq H$ for all x in G.

You will recall that if H is a subgroup of a group G, the collection of right cosets of H in G is not necessarily the same as the collection of left cosets of H (Example 6). That this cannot happen when H is normal is proved next.

Theorem 14 H is a normal subgroup of G if, and only if, every right coset Hx is also a left coset xH.

Proof: Suppose $H \triangle G$. Then $x^{-1}Hx = H$ for all x in G. Thus $Hx = xH$. Conversely, if $Hx = yH$, then x belongs to yH, which implies that $xH = yH$. Thus $Hx = xH$ (and hence $x^{-1}Hx = H$) for all x in G. Therefore H is normal.

Exercise 15 Suppose H and K are normal subgroups of a group G. Prove that $H \cap K$ is also normal in G.

Example 14 Every subgroup of an Abelian group is normal. In particular, every subgroup of a cyclic group is normal.

Example 15 In the group of symmetries of the square, we have already noted that the subsets $K_1 = \{I, H\}$ and $K_3 = \{I, H, V, R'\}$ are subgroups. Now K_3 is also a normal subgroup while K_1 is not (show this). However, K_1 is normal in K_3.

Remark 16 It is clear that if H, K, and G are groups such that $H \subset K \subset G$ and $H \triangle G$, then H will also be normal in K. But suppose $H \subset K \subset G$ and $H \triangle K$. When is $H \triangle G$? Certainly not always, as is seen in Example 15. Also, when is $K \triangle G$? We shall have more to say on this later.

Example 16 The subset $H = \{P_1, P_2, \ldots, P_{12}\}$ is a normal subgroup of the group S_4. (That H is a subgroup follows by inspecting the upper left corner of Table 2.)

Definition 15 Let G be a group and A a nonempty subset of G. We call A a *complex*. If A and B are two complexes, by the product AB we mean the set of all products ab, a in A and b in B.

Note: To say that $AB = BA$ where A and B are complexes of G, does not mean that $ab = ba$ for all a in A and b in B; but rather that, given a_1b_1 in AB, there exists $b'a'$ (not necessarily $b_1 a_1$) in BA such that $a_1 b_1 = b'a'$, and conversely. In particular, if B consists of a single element x, to say that $Ax = xA$ does not mean $ax = xa$ for all a in A.

Exercise 16 Suppose H and K are subgroups of a group G. Show that HK is a subgroup of G if, and only if, $HK = KH$.

Exercise 17 Suppose G is a group, H and K subgroups of G. Prove that HK is a subgroup of G if either H or K is normal in G.

Exercise 18 In Exercise 17, suppose H and K are both normal in G. Prove that HK is normal in G.

The preceding exercises give us conditions in order that HK be a subgroup of a group G when H and K are subgroups of G. But what about the order of HK? In future discussions we shall need this information. We obtain it now.

Note: We shall henceforth denote the number of elements in a finite set S by $|S|$.

Theorem 15 Suppose H and K are finite subgroups of a group G. Then $|HK| = \dfrac{|H| \cdot |K|}{|H \cap K|}$. (It should be noted here that we are *not* assuming that HK is a subgroup of G.)

Proof: Suppose x belongs to $H \cap K$ and hk belongs to HK. We may write $hk = hxx^{-1}k$. Now hx belongs to H (x does) and $x^{-1}k$ belongs to K (x^{-1} does). Thus the element hk appears in HK at least $|H \cap K|$ times. If $hk = h_1 k_1$, then $kk_1^{-1} = h^{-1}h_1$, which is an element of $H \cap K$. Therefore $h_1 = hkk_1^{-1}$ and $k_1 = h_1^{-1}hk$, which implies hk appears in HK at most $|H \cap K|$ times. Hence the element hk appears in HK exactly $|H \cap K|$ times. It follows that the number of distinct elements in HK is the product of the number of elements in H and the number of elements in K, divided by the number of times a given element appears in HK.

Exercise 19 Let G be a group and $Z(G) = \{a$ in $G; ax = xa$ for all x in $G\}$. Prove that $Z(G)$ is a normal subgroup of G. ($Z(G)$ is called the *center* of G.)

Exercise 20 Suppose G is a group and x and y belong to G. The element $x^{-1}y^{-1}xy$ is called the *commutator* of x and y. Prove that the set G' of all finite products of such commutators froms a normal subgroup of G. (G' is called the *commutator subgroup*, or *derived group* of G.)

We have seen that if H is a subgroup of a group G and $xH = Hx$ for all x in G, then H is a normal subgroup. Thus, in the case H is not normal in G, $xH = Hx$ does not hold for some element x in G. If we confine our attention to just those elements x of G for which xH and Hx are indeed equal, we are led to some very interesting and very useful results. We do this here in a more general setting, in that we merely assume H to be a complex of G.

Definition 16   Let G be a group and H a complex of G. The set of elements in G that commute with H is called the *normalizer* of H in G and is denoted by $N_G(H)$.

Note: A subgroup H of a group G is normal in G if, and only if, $N_G(H) = G$.

Theorem 16 $N_G(H)$ is a subgroup of G. Furthermore, $[G:N_G(H)]$ = the number of conjugates of H.

Proof: Let x and y belong to $N_G(H)$. Then $Hx = xH$ and $Hy = yH$, or $H = xHx^{-1}$ and $H = yHy^{-1}$. Thus $xHx^{-1} = yHy^{-1}$, which implies that $Hx^{-1}y = x^{-1}yH$. Therefore $x^{-1}y$ belongs to $N_G(H)$ and hence $N_G(H)$ is a subgroup. Next, let $D = N_G(H)$, $S = \{Dx; x$ in $G\}$, and $T = \{x^{-1}Hx; x$ in $G\}$. Define $f:S \to T$ by $f(Dx) = x^{-1}Hx$. (The reader should show that f is well-defined.) f is clearly onto. We show f is 1-1 as follows: Suppose $f(Dx) = f(Dy)$; that is, suppose $x^{-1}Hx = y^{-1}Hy$. Then $yx^{-1}H = Hyx^{-1}$. Thus yx^{-1} belongs to D, implying y belongs to Dx. Therefore $Dx = Dy$. Hence the number of conjugates of H is equal to the number of right cosets of $N_G(H)$, which is $[G:N_G(H)]$.

Theorem 16 is one of extreme importance in obtaining future results and we emphasize it with our next example.

Example 17   Consider again the group G of symmetries of the square (Example 3) and let K be the complex $\{R, H, D'\}$. We first determine $N_G(K)$. By inspecting Table 1 we find that the only elements x in G for which $xK = Kx$ are I and R'. Therefore $N_G(K) = \{I, R'\}$, which is clearly a subgroup of G. Next we determine the left cosets of $N_G(K)$. These are the sets $\{I, R'\}$, $\{R, R''\}$, $\{H, V\}$ and $\{D, D'\}$. Finally, we see that the conjugates of K are $\{R, H, D'\}$, $\{R, V, D\}$, $\{R'', H, D\}$, and $\{R'', V, D'\}$. Thus the number of conjugates of K is equal to the number of left cosets of $N_G(K)$, which of course is $[G:N_G(K)]$.

Exercise 21   Let G be a group and a belong to G. Show that the normalizer of a is a group containing the cyclic group generated by a as a normal subgroup.

1-6.   HOMOMORPHISMS
AND
QUOTIENT GROUPS

In Definition 12 we introduced the concept of isomorphism. A much more general notion is that of homomorphism. We define it here and develop several important results in connection with normal subgroups.

Definition 17   Let G and $\overline{G}$ be groups with respect to $*$ and $*'$ respectively. Let φ be a mapping from G into $\overline{G}$. If $\varphi(a*b) = \varphi(a) *' \varphi(b)$ for all a and b in G, then we call φ a *homomorphism*. The set $\overline{H} = \{\,\overline{x}$ in $\overline{G}; \varphi(x) = \overline{x}$ for some x in $G\}$ is called the *homomorphic image* of G under φ.

Note: If φ is a homomorphism of G onto $\overline{G}$ then $\overline{H} = \overline{G}$ and we say that G and $\overline{G}$ are homomorphic.

Example 18   For G and $\overline{G}$ any groups, the mapping $\varphi : G \to \overline{G}$ defined by $\varphi(x) = \overline{e}$, $\overline{e}$ the identity of $\overline{G}$, is clearly a homomorphism.

Example 19   Any isomorphism of G onto $\overline{G}$ is a homomorphism of G onto $\overline{G}$.

Example 20   Consider the following groups: S_4, and $G = \{1, -1\}$ (under multiplication). Define the mapping $\varphi : S_4 \to G$ by $\varphi(P_i) = 1$, $1 \leqslant i \leqslant 12$, and $\varphi(P_j) = -1$, $13 \leqslant j \leqslant 24$. S_4 and G are homomorphic under φ.

Theorem 17   Let φ be a homomorphism of G into $\overline{G}$ (G and $\overline{G}$ groups). Then $\overline{H}$, the homomorphic image of G in $\overline{G}$, is a subgroup of $\overline{G}$.

Proof: Let $\overline{a}$ and $\overline{b}$ belong to $\overline{H}$ and let a and b be elements of G such that $\varphi(a) = \overline{a}$, $\varphi(b) = \overline{b}$. Now $\varphi(ab)$ belongs to $\overline{H}$ and $\varphi(ab) = \varphi(a)\varphi(b) = \overline{ab}$. Therefore $\overline{ab}$ is in $\overline{H}$. Next, let e be the identity of G and $\overline{x}$ belong to $\overline{H}$ where $\varphi(x) = \overline{x}$, x in G. Then $\overline{x} = \varphi(x) = \varphi(ex) = \varphi(e)\varphi(x) = \varphi(e)\overline{x}$, which implies that $\varphi(e)$ is the identity of $\overline{H}$. (We shall denote $\varphi(e)$ by $\overline{e}$.) Finally, let $\overline{y}$ belong to $\overline{H}$ where $\varphi(y) = \overline{y}$, y in G. Then $\overline{e} = \varphi(e) = \varphi(yy^{-1}) = \varphi(y)\varphi(y^{-1}) = y\varphi(y^{-1})$, implying that $\varphi(y^{-1}) = (\overline{y})^{-1}$.

Note: One could speak of a homomorphism φ from a group G into a *set S* having defined on it a binary operation $*'$. Here, as in Theorem 17, it is easily shown that the homomorphic image of G under φ is a group. However, it is necessary to verify the associative property in this case.

Exercise 22   Suppose φ is a homomorphism of G into $\overline{G}$ and ψ a homomorphism of $\overline{G}$ into $\overline{\overline{G}}$. Prove that the mapping $\psi\varphi : G \to \overline{\overline{G}}$ defined by $(\psi\varphi)(x) = \psi(\varphi(x))$ is a homomorphism of G into $\overline{\overline{G}}$. Also prove that if φ and ψ are both *onto*, then so is the homomorphism $\psi\varphi$.

Definition 18   Suppose G is a group homomorphic to $\overline{G}$ under a homomorphism φ. Let K be the set of elements k in G such that $\varphi(k) = \overline{e}$, the identity of $\overline{G}$. K is called the *kernel* of the homomorphism φ.

Example 21   The *kernel* of the homomorphism of Example 18 is all of G; of Example 20, it is $\{P_1, P_2, \ldots, P_{12}\}$.

Theorem 18   The kernel K of a homomorphism φ from a group G onto a group $\overline{G}$ is a normal subgroup of G. Furthermore, two elements of G have the same image in $\overline{G}$ if, and only if, they belong to the same right (left) coset of K.

Proof: Suppose k_1 and k_2 belong to K. Then $\varphi(k_1) = \bar{e}$ and $\varphi(k_2) = \bar{e}$. Now $\varphi(k_1 k_2^{-1}) = \varphi(k_1) \varphi(k_2^{-1}) = \bar{e} [\varphi(k_2)]^{-1} = \bar{e}\bar{e} = \bar{e}$, which implies $k_1 k_2^{-1}$ belongs to K. Thus K is a subgroup of G. Next, let x belong to G and k belong to K. Suppose $\varphi(x) = a$. Then $\varphi(x^{-1} kx) = \varphi(x^{-1}) \varphi(k) \varphi(x) = a^{-1}\bar{e}a = \bar{e}$. This implies that $x^{-1} kx$ is an element of K and so K is normal in G.

To complete the proof of the theorem, let x and y belong to G where $\varphi(x) = \varphi(y) = a$. Then $\varphi(xy^{-1}) = \bar{e}$, implying that xy^{-1} belongs to K. Thus x belongs to Ky and x and y are in the same right coset of K. Conversely, if x is in Ky, then $x = ky$, k in K. Suppose $\varphi(y) = a$. Then $\varphi(x) = \varphi(ky) = \varphi(k) \varphi(y) = \bar{e}a = a$, and we see that x and y have the same image in G.

Exercise 23 Let K be the kernel of a homomorphism π of a group G onto a group G'. If $K = \{e\}$, prove that π is an isomorphism.

The following example serves to introduce a whole new class of groups.

Example 22 Consider the subgroups $K_1 = \{I, H\}$ and $K_4 = \{I, R'\}$ of the group of symmetries of the square. In Example 6 we found the right cosets of K_1 to

TABLE 6

	$\{I, H\}$	$\{R, D'\}$	$\{R', V\}$	$\{R'', D\}$
$\{I, H\}$	$\{I, H\}$	$\{R, D'\}$	$\{R', V\}$	$\{R'', D\}$
$\{R, D'\}$	$\{R, D, D', R''\}$	$\{R', H, V, I\}$	$\{R'', D', D, R\}$	$\{I, V, H, R'\}$
$\{R', V\}$	$\{R', V\}$	$\{R'', D\}$	$\{I, H\}$	$\{R, D'\}$
$\{R'', D\}$	$\{R'', D', D, R\}$	$\{I, V, H, R'\}$	$\{R, D, D', R''\}$	$\{R', H, V, I\}$

be $\{I, H\}$, $\{R, D'\}$, $\{R', V\}$, and $\{R'', D\}$. The right cosets of K_4 are $\{I, R'\}$, $\{R, R''\}$, $\{H, V\}$, and $\{D, D'\}$. Table 6 gives the product of any two right cosets of K_1, and Table 7 the product of any two right cosets of K_4.

TABLE 7

	$\{I, R'\}$	$\{R, R''\}$	$\{H, V\}$	$\{D, D'\}$
$\{I, R'\}$	$\{I, R'\}$	$\{R, R''\}$	$\{H, V\}$	$\{D, D'\}$
$\{R, R''\}$	$\{R, R''\}$	$\{R', I\}$	$\{D, D'\}$	$\{V, H\}$
$\{H, V\}$	$\{H, V\}$	$\{D', D\}$	$\{I, R'\}$	$\{R'', R\}$
$\{D, D'\}$	$\{D, D'\}$	$\{H, V\}$	$\{R, R''\}$	$\{I, R'\}$

One notices immediately that the product of any two right cosets of K_4 is again a right coset of K_4. But not so for K_1. As is seen in our next theorem, the reason for this tremendous difference is the fact that K_4 is normal. The reader may wish to verify that K_4 is the center for the group of symmetries of the square. (See Exercise 19.)

Theorem 19 Let G be a group and N a subgroup of G. N is normal in G if, and only if, the product of any two right cosets of N is a right coset of N.

Proof: Suppose $N \vartriangle G$ and let Nx and Ny be right cosets of N. Then $NxNy = N(xN)y = N(Nx)y = NNxy = Nxy$. Conversely, suppose the product of any two right cosets of N is again a right coset of N. Then for x in G, $NxNx^{-1}$ is a right coset, and it contains the element $exex^{-1} = e$. Thus $NxNx^{-1} = N$, which implies that $xNx^{-1} \subseteq N$, which implies that N is normal in G (Remark 15).

Remark 17 The equation $NxNy = Nxy$ defines a binary operation on the collection of right cosets of a normal subgroup N. Remarkably, with this concept of "product," these cosets form a group, as we show next.

Theorem 20 The cosets of any normal subgroup N of a group G form a group with respect to multiplication of cosets as defined above.

Proof: Since $(NxNy)Nz = NxyNz = N(xy)z = Nx(yz) = NxNyz = Nx(NyNz)$, the product is associative. $N = Ne$ is the left identity, since $(Ne)(Nx) = Nex = Nx$, for all cosets Nx. Finally, we have $Nx^{-1}Nx = Nx^{-1}x = Ne = N$, which implies that Nx^{-1} is the left inverse of Nx.

Definition 19 The group of cosets of N is called the *quotient group* (factor group) of G by N and is denoted by G/N.

Thus the quotient group of the group of symmetries of the square by its center is the collection of cosets of K_4 given in Example 22, and Table 7 is the multiplication table for this quotient group.

Example 23 In S_4, the subset $N = \{P_1, P_2, P_3, P_4\}$ is a normal subgroup of the group $G = \{P_1, P_2, \ldots, P_{12}\}$. The right cosets of N in G are $N, A = \{P_5, P_8, P_9, P_{12}\}$, and $B = \{P_6, P_7, P_{10}, P_{11}\}$. Thus $G/N = \{N, A, B\}$. (The reader should verify all of this.)

Note: $|G/N| = [G:N]$.

A problem of interest is the following: when is the quotient group of a group G by a normal subgroup N, cyclic? In the above example we have a cyclic quotient group (why?) with both G and N noncyclic. The reader may wish to pursue this problem further.

Theorem 21 Let G be a group and N a normal subgroup of G. Then the mapping $\varphi: G \to G/N$ defined by $\varphi(x) = Nx$ is a homomorphism of G onto G/N and N is the kernel of φ.

Proof: φ is clearly onto. Suppose $\varphi(x) = Nx$, $\varphi(y) = Ny$. Then $\varphi(xy) = Nxy = NxNy = \varphi(x)\varphi(y)$. Therefore φ is a homomorphism. Next, suppose x belongs to G and $\varphi(x) = N$ (the identity of G/N). Since $\varphi(x)$ also equals Nx, we have x belongs to N. Conversely, if x belongs to N, then $\varphi(x) = Nx = N$. Therefore N is the kernel of φ.

Note: The homomorphism φ as defined in Theorem 21 is usually referred to as the *natural homomorphism* of G onto G/N.

Theorem 22   Suppose φ is a homomorphism of a group G onto a group $\bar{G}$ and K is the kernel of φ. Then $\bar{G}$ is isomorphic to G/K.

Proof: Define $\pi: G/K \to \bar{G}$ by $\pi(Kx) = \bar{x}$, where $\bar{x}$ is the image of x under the homomorphism φ. We show π is an isomorphism. (The reader should show that π is well-defined.) Clearly, π is onto. Suppose $\pi(Kx) = \bar{x}$ and $\pi(Ky) = \bar{y}$. If $\bar{x} = \bar{y}$, then $\varphi(x) = \varphi(y)$, which implies that x and y belong to the same coset of K (Theorem 18). Thus $Kx = Ky$ and π is 1-1. Finally, since $\pi(KxKy) = \pi(Kxy) = \overline{xy} = \varphi(xy) = \varphi(x)\varphi(y) = \bar{x}\bar{y} = \pi(Kx)\pi(Ky)$, π is an isomorphism.

The results of Theorems 18, 21, and 22 are of such importance that we re-state them here:

(i)   The kernel of any homomorphism is a normal subgroup.

(ii)   Any normal subgroup is the kernel of a homomorphism.

(iii)   To within isomorphism, the only homomorphic images of a group G are the quotient groups G/N, N any normal subgroup in G.

Example 24   Let us find all homomorphic images of the group G of symmetries of the square. These are (to within isomorphism) the quotient groups G/N, $N \triangle G$. Thus we must find all normal subgroups of G. It has already been shown that $K_2 = \{I,R,R',R''\}$, $K_3 = \{I,H,V,R'\}$, and $K_4 = \{I,R'\}$ are normal. Of course, so are G and $\{I\}$. That $K_5 = \{I,R',D,D'\}$ is also normal may be verified easily. Therefore the quotient groups of G are the groups

$$G/K_2 = \{\{I,R,R',R''\}, \{H,V,D,D'\}\}$$
$$G/K_3 = \{\{I,H,V,R'\}, \{R,R'',D,D'\}\}$$
$$G/K_4 = \{\{I,R'\}, \{R,R''\}, \{H,V\}, \{D,D'\}\}$$
$$G/K_5 = \{\{I,R',D,D'\}, \{R,R'',H,V\}\}, G/G = \{G\}$$
and
$$G/\{I\} = \{\{I\}, \{R\}, \{R'\}, \{R''\}, \{H\}, \{V\}, \{D\}, \{D'\}\}$$

Now K_3 and K_5 are isomorphic (thus so are G/K_3 and G/K_5). Hence (to within isomorphism) the homomorphic images of G are G/K_2, G/K_3, G/K_4, G/G, and $G/\{I\}$. These last two correspond to the homomorphisms obtained by mapping all elements onto the identity and every element onto itself, respectively.

Note: We emphasize the following: If N_1 and N_2 are normal subgroups of a group G and N_1 and N_2 are isomorphic, then G/N_1 and G/N_2 are isomor-phic. (Is the converse also true?)

Exercise 24   Suppose that G is a cyclic group of order n. How many homomor-phic images of G are there?

Exercise 25   Suppose G is a cyclic group and H a subgroup of G such that $[G:H] = m$. Prove that G/H is cyclic of order m (see comment preceding Theorem 21).

In Exercise 20 you were introduced to the derived group G' of a group G. The following are important properties of this group.

Exercise 26   Prove that G/G' is Abelian.

Exercise 27   Suppose N is normal in G and G/N is Abelian. Prove that $G' \subseteq N$./
We end this section with the following useful theorem.

Theorem 23   Suppose G is a group and N a normal subgroup of G. There is a 1-1 correspondence between subgroups H of G containing N and subgroups H' of G/N. Furthermore, H is normal in G if, and only if, H' is normal in G/N. Also, $[G:H] = [G/N:H']$.

Proof: Consider the natural homomorphism φ from G onto G/N. Clearly, if H is any subgroup of G, then $\varphi(H) = H'$ is a subgroup of G/N (Theorem 17). Suppose H' is a subgroup of G/N and H is the subset of G such that $\varphi(H) = H'$. Since $\varphi(N) = N$ belongs to H', H contains N. We show H is a subgroup of G. Let x and y belong to H. Then $\varphi(x)$ and $\varphi(y)$ belong to H'. Since H' is a group, $\varphi(x)\varphi(y)$ is in H'. But $\varphi(x)\varphi(y) = \varphi(xy)$. Therefore xy belongs to H. Finally, x in H implies $\varphi(x)$ in H', which implies $\varphi(x)^{-1} = \varphi(x^{-1})$ is in H'. Thus x^{-1} is in H and so H is a subgroup of G. Now if we suppose K is a subgroup of G containing N such that $\varphi(K)$ is also H', then we must have $K = H$. For let h belong H. Then $\varphi(h)$ belongs to H', which is equal to $\varphi(K)$. But then h must also be in K, implying that $H \subseteq K$. Similarly, we have $K \subseteq H$. Next, suppose that H is normal in G and x is an element of G/N. There exists g in G such that $\varphi(g) = x$. Thus $x^{-1}H'x = \varphi(g^{-1})\varphi(H)\varphi(g) = \varphi(g^{-1}Hg) = \varphi(H) = H'$, which implies that H' is normal in G/N. If $H' \triangle G/N$ and g belongs to G, then $\varphi(g^{-1}Hg) = \varphi(g)^{-1}H'\varphi(g) = H'$. This implies that $g^{-1}Hg = H$, and so $H \triangle G$. It is clear that $[G:H] = [G/N:H']$.

1-7.   AUTOMORPHISMS

In this section we discuss a special class of isomorphisms of a group G.

Definition 20   An *automorphism* α of a group G is an isomorphism of G onto itself.

Theorem 24   Let $A(G)$ be the set of automorphisms of a group G. Then $A(G)$ is a group with respect to product of mappings.

Proof: Since $A(G)$ is a subset of the set of all 1-1 mappings of G onto itself, we need only show that $A(G)$ is closed and that every element of $A(G)$ has an inverse in $A(G)$. (See Example 4 and Remark 4.) Let α_1 and α_2 belong to $A(G)$. Clearly, $\alpha_1\alpha_2$ is 1-1 and onto. Let x and y be elements of G. Then $(\alpha_1\alpha_2)(xy) = \alpha_1(\alpha_2(xy)) = \alpha_1(\alpha_2(x)\alpha_2(y)) = \alpha_1(\alpha_2(x))\alpha_1(\alpha_2(y)) = (\alpha_1\alpha_2)(x)$ $(\alpha_1\alpha_2)(y)$. Finally, suppose α belongs to $A(G)$. Then $\alpha^{-1}(xy) = \alpha^{-1}[(\alpha\alpha^{-1})(x)$ $(\alpha\alpha^{-1})(y)] = \alpha^{-1}[\alpha(\alpha^{-1}(x)\alpha^{-1}(y))] = (\alpha^{-1}\alpha)(\alpha^{-1}(x)\alpha^{-1}(y)) = \alpha^{-1}(x)\alpha^{-1}(y)$, implying that α^{-1} belongs to $A(G)$.

Definition 21   In any group G, the element $a^{-1}xa$ is called the *conjugate* of x by a. (See Definition 13.)

Theorem 25   Let G be a group and a belong to G. The mapping $\pi_a : G \to G$ defined by $\pi_a(x) = a^{-1}xa$ is an automorphism.

   Proof: π_a is onto, since, given y in G, $\pi_a(aya^{-1}) = y$. Suppose $\pi_a(x) = a^{-1}$ xa and $\pi_a(y) = a^{-1}ya$. If $a^{-1}xa = a^{-1}ya$, then $x = y$. Therefore π_a is 1-1. Finally, we have $\pi_a(xy) = a^{-1}(xy)a = a^{-1}xaa^{-1}ya = \pi_a(x)\pi_a(y)$. Thus π_a is an automorphism of G.

Definition 22   The automorphisms π_a are called *inner automorphisms*; all other automorphisms are called *outer*.

Theorem 26   The inner automorphisms of a group G form a normal subgroup $I(G)$ of the group $A(G)$.

   Proof: Let π_a and π_b belong to $I(G)$. Then $(\pi_a\pi_b)(x) = \pi_a(b^{-1}xb) = a^{-1}$ $b^{-1}xba = (ba)^{-1}x(ba) = \pi_{ba}(x)$, so that $\pi_a\pi_b$ belongs to $I(G)$. Also, $(\pi_{a^{-1}}\pi_a)(x) = \pi_{a^{-1}}(a^{-1}xa) = (a^{-1})^{-1}(a^{-1}xa)a^{-1} = x$, implying that $\pi_{a^{-1}} = \pi_a^{-1}$. Therefore $I(G)$ is a subgroup of $A(G)$. To show $I(G) \triangle A(G)$, let α belong to $A(G)$, π_a belong to $I(G)$, and x belong to G. Then $(\alpha^{-1}\pi_a\alpha)(x) = \alpha^{-1}(a^{-1}\alpha(x)a) = \alpha^{-1}(a^{-1})x\alpha^{-1}(a) = \pi_{\alpha^{-1}(a)}(x)$. Thus $\alpha^{-1}\pi_a\alpha = \pi_{\alpha^{-1}(a)}$ belongs to $I(G)$ and we have $I(G)$ is normal in $A(G)$.

Theorem 27   Let G be a group and H a subgroup of G. H is normal in G if, and only if, it is invariant under all inner automorphisms of G (that is, H contains the conjugates of each of its elements by all elements of G).

   Proof: See Definition 14.

   Note: One perhaps sees from Theorem 27 why normal subgroups are also referred to as invariant, or self-conjugate subgroups.

   The following example illustrates the previous notions concerning automorphisms.

Example 25   Table 8 lists the inner automorphisms of the group G of symmetries of the square. Here we have $\pi_I = \pi_R$, $\pi_R = \pi_{R''}$, $\pi_H = \pi_V$ and $\pi_D = \pi_{D'}$.

All other automorphisms of G are outer. These are given in Table 9. Observe that $[A(G):I(G)] = 2$. This shows that $I(G)$ is normal in $A(G)$. (The reader should prove in general that, if G is a group and H is a subgroup of G of index 2, then $H \triangle G$.) Observe too what the inner automorphisms do to the normal subgroups of G.

TABLE 8

X	$\pi_I(X)$	$\pi_R(X)$	$\pi_H(X)$	$\pi_D(X)$
I.	I	I	I	I
R	R	R	R''	R''
R'	R'	R'	R'	R'
R''	R''	R''	R	R
H	H	V	H	V
V	V	H	V	H
D	D	D	D	D
D'	D'	D	D	D'

TABLE 9

X	$\alpha_1(X)$	$\alpha_2(X)$	$\alpha_3(X)$	$\alpha_4(X)$
I	I	I	I	I
R	R	R	R''	R''
R'	R'	R'	R'	R'
R''	R''	R''	R	R
H	D	D'	D	D'
V	D'	D	D'	D
D	V	H	H	V
D'	H	V	V	H

We have seen that every group is isomorphic to a permutation group (Theorem 12). In particular, one can show that $G = \{I, R, R', R'', H, V, D, D'\}$ and $A(G) = \{\pi_I, \pi_R, \pi_H, \pi_D, \alpha_1, \alpha_2, \alpha_3, \alpha_4\}$ are isomorphic. (The reader *should* show this.)

Exercise 28 Show that the elements of a group G may be divided into classes of conjugate elements, where the number of elements of a class is a divisor of the order of G (when G is finite). Show also that every element in $Z(G)$ forms a class by itself. (This is a most important result and will be applied several times in later sections.)

Exercise 29 Suppose G is any group. Prove that the mapping $\varphi:G \to I(G)$ defined by $\varphi(a) = \pi_{a^{-1}}$ is a homomorphism of G onto $I(G)$ whose kernel is $Z(G)$. (In particular, verify this for Example 25.)

Exercise 30 Prove that $G/Z(G)$ is isomorphic to $I(G)$.

Exercise 31 Show that the only inner automorphism of an Abelian group is the identity automorphism.

Exercise 32 Determine all automorphisms of a finite cyclic group.

2

Solvable Groups

2-1. PERMUTATIONS
ALTERNATING GROUPS

We now return to the symmetric groups S_n, first discussed in Example 4.
In Example 5, in the case $n = 4$, symbols such as $\begin{pmatrix} 1\ 2\ 3\ 4 \\ 4\ 3\ 1\ 2 \end{pmatrix}$ were used to
represent the permutations on the set S containing 4 elements, arbitrarily la-
beled 1, 2, 3, 4. Here, $\begin{pmatrix} 1\ 2\ 3\ 4 \\ 4\ 3\ 1\ 2 \end{pmatrix}$ is the permutation which maps 1 onto 4, 2 onto
3, 3 onto 1, and 4 onto 2. Of course, this notion may be extended to $S =$
$\{1, 2, \ldots, n\}$ for any positive integer n. We wish now to improve on this
method of representing permutations.

Definition 23 A permutation P on a set $S = \{x_1, x_2, \ldots, x_n\}$ will be called
a *cycle* of length m, if S has a subset $\{y_1, y_2, \ldots, y_m\}$ such that $P(y_i) =$
y_{i+1}, $1 \leqslant i < m$ and $P(y_m) = y_1$, while $P(y_j) = y_j$, $m < j \leqslant n$. Such a cycle will
be denoted by $(y_1, y_2, \ldots, y_m)$.

If an element of S is mapped onto itself by a permutation P, we shall omit
it in our notation for P (except for the identity permutation, which will be de-
noted by (1)). Thus, for $P = \begin{pmatrix} 1\ 2\ 3\ 4\ 5 \\ 3\ 2\ 1\ 4\ 5 \end{pmatrix}$ we write (13). In S_4, (124) is the permutation that maps 1 onto 2, 2 onto 4, 4 onto 1, and 3 onto 3.

Now consider the permutations $P_1 = \begin{pmatrix} 1\ 2\ 3\ 4 \\ 4\ 3\ 2\ 1 \end{pmatrix}$ and $P_2 = \begin{pmatrix} 1\ 2\ 3\ 4\ 5 \\ 3\ 5\ 4\ 1\ 2 \end{pmatrix}$. Clearly,

P_1 and P_2 cannot be written as cycles. But $\begin{pmatrix} 1\ 2\ 3\ 4 \\ 4\ 3\ 2\ 1 \end{pmatrix} = \begin{pmatrix} 1\ 2\ 3\ 4 \\ 4\ 2\ 3\ 1 \end{pmatrix} \begin{pmatrix} 1\ 2\ 3\ 4 \\ 1\ 3\ 2\ 4 \end{pmatrix} =$

$(14)(23)$, and $\begin{pmatrix} 1\ 2\ 3\ 4\ 5 \\ 3\ 5\ 4\ 1\ 2 \end{pmatrix} = \begin{pmatrix} 1\ 2\ 3\ 4\ 5 \\ 3\ 2\ 4\ 1\ 5 \end{pmatrix} \begin{pmatrix} 1\ 2\ 3\ 4\ 5 \\ 1\ 5\ 3\ 4\ 2 \end{pmatrix} = (134)(25)$. Thus it appears that if a permutation cannot itself be written as a cycle, then it can be written as a product of cycles. (This indeed is the case and the reader should show it. That is, show that if P is a permutation on the set $S = \{x_1, x_2, \ldots, x_n\}$, then P may be written uniquely as a product of cycles on disjoint subsets of S.)

We note that since $(x_1\ x_2 \cdots x_n) = (x_1\ x_n)(x_1\ x_{n-1}) \cdots (x_1\ x_2)$, every permutation on S may be written as a product of cycles, each having length 2. (Such a cycle is called a *transposition*.) Of course, these are not cycles on disjoint subsets of S. One also loses uniqueness in this case. For example, $(124) = (14)(12)$ and $(12)(24)$; $(134) = (14)(13)$ and $(13)(34)$.

Next, consider the polynomial Δ in the variables $x_1, x_2, \ldots, x_n$ given by

$$\begin{aligned}
\Delta = (x_1 - x_2)(x_1 - x_3)(x_1 - x_4) &\cdots (x_1 - x_n) \\
\times\ (x_2 - x_3)(x_2 - x_4) &\cdots (x_2 - x_n) \\
\times\ (x_3 - x_4) &\cdots (x_3 - x_n) \\
\times\ (x_{n-1} &- x_n)
\end{aligned}$$

If the permutation $(x_1 x_2)$ is applied to Δ we notice that Δ is changed to the product

$$\begin{aligned}
(x_2 - x_1)(x_2 - x_3)(x_2 - x_4) &\cdots (x_2 - x_n) \\
\times\ (x_1 - x_3)(x_1 - x_4) &\cdots (x_1 - x_n) \\
\times\ (x_3 - x_4) &\cdots (x_3 - x_n) \\
\times\ (x_{n-1} &- x_n)
\end{aligned}$$

That is, Δ is changed to $-\Delta$. In general, for any permutation P, we have $P(\Delta) = \Delta$ or $-\Delta$.

Definition 24   A permutation P is said to be *even* if $P(\Delta) = \Delta$; *odd* if $P(\Delta) = -\Delta$.

Remark 18   Every transposition is an odd permutation. Also, the product of two even or two odd permutations is even; the product of an even and odd permutation is odd. Thus an even permutation is one than can be written as a product of an even number of transpositions, and an odd permutation one that can be written as a product of an odd number of transpositions.

Exercise 33   Write the elements of S_4 as products of transpositions, thus showing that $P_1, P_2, \ldots, P_{12}$ are the even permutations.

Note: A cycle of length m is even when m is odd; odd when m is even.

Theorem 28   Denote by A_n the set of all even permutations in S_n. Then A_n is a normal subgroup of S_n and $|A_n| = \dfrac{n!}{2}$.

Proof: Define $\varphi: S_n \to \{1,-1\}$ by $\varphi(P) = 1$ if P is even and $\varphi(P) = -1$ if P is odd. One shows easily that φ is a homomorphism of S_n onto $\{1,-1\}$. Clearly, A_n is the kernel of φ. Thus A_n is normal in S_n by Theorem 18. Now S_n/A_n is isomorphic to $\{1,-1\}$. Therefore $[S_n : A_n] = 2$, which implies that $|A_n| = \dfrac{n!}{2}$.

A_n is called the *alternating group* on n symbols. Later we shall show that the alternating groups afford us with examples of a certain class of groups.

Exercise 34 Find the derived group of S_4. (See Exercise 20.) Generalize your result to S_n.

Exercise 35 Divide A_4 into classes of conjugate elements. (See Exercise 28.) What is $Z(A_4)$?

2-2. SIMPLE GROUPS

In this section we introduce the groups that are referred to as simple groups.

Definition 25 A subgroup H of a group G is a *maximal normal subgroup* if H is a normal subgroup and there exists no proper normal subgroup K of G which properly contains H.

Theorem 29 is a corollary to Theorem 23, but we emphasize it now.

Theorem 29 Suppose H is normal in G and K a subgroup of G such that $H \subset K \subset G$. Then K is normal in G if, and only if, K/H is normal in G/H.

Proof: Suppose $K \triangle G . H \triangle G$ and $H \subset K \subset G$ imply that H is normal in K. Thus K/H is a group (clearly, a subgroup of G/H). We wish to show that K/H is a normal subgroup of G/H. Let Hg belong to G/H and Hk belong to K/H. Then $(Hg)^{-1}(Hk)(Hg) = (Hg^{-1})(Hk)(Hg) = Hg^{-1}kg$ belongs to K/H (since $g^{-1}kg$ is in K). Therefore $K/H \triangle G/H$. Conversely, suppose $K/H \triangle G/H$. Then if Hg belongs to G/H and Hk belongs to K/H, $(Hg)^{-1}(Hk)(Hg) = Hg^{-1}kg$ belongs to K/H. Now the elements of K/H are of the form Hx, where x is in K. Thus we have $g^{-1}kg$ belongs to K, which implies that K is normal in G.

Remark 19 It follows from Theorem 29 that H is a maximal normal subgroup of G if, and only if, the quotient group G/H contains no proper normal subgroups. Groups with this property are of special interest.

Definition 26 A *simple group* is a group containing no proper normal subgroups.

Example 26 Groups of prime order are simple groups.

Example 27 The alternating group A_4 is not simple since it contains the normal subgroup $N = \{P_1, P_2, P_3, P_4\}$. (See Example 23.) Clearly, S_4/A_4 is a simple group.

Exercise 36   Suppose G is a finite Abelian simple group. Prove that G is a cyclic group of prime order.

We have called a group G cyclic if it contains an element x such that every element of G can be written as a power of x. More generally, suppose G is a group and $x_1, x_2, \ldots$, are elements of G. If every element of G can be expressed as a finite product of terms of the form $x_1^{e_1} x_2^{e_2} \cdots$, then we say that $x_1, x_2, \ldots$, generate G. Clearly, every finite group is generated by a finite set $\{x_1, x_2, \ldots, x_m\}$.

Exercise 37   Show that the cycles $(12), (13), \ldots, (1n)$ generate S_n.

Theorem 30   The cycles $(123), (124), \ldots, (12n)$ generate the alternating group $A_n, n > 2$.

Proof: The elements of A_n may be written as a product of an even number of transpositions, each of which is a product of cycles of the form $(1n)$ (Exercise 37). Thus we need only show that a product $(1j)(1k)$ where $2 \leqslant j$, $k \leqslant n$, may be expressed as a product of elements of the form $(12n)$ or $(12n)^{-1} = (1n2)$. For $j = k$ we have $(1j)(1k) = (1) = (123)(132)$. For $j \neq k$ and $j = 2$ we have $(1j)(1k) = (12)(1k) = (1k2)$. For $j \neq k$ and $k = 2$, $(1j)(1k) = (1j)(12) = (12j)$. And finally, for $j \neq k$, j and $k \geqslant 3$, we have $(1j)(1k) = (1j)(12)(12)(1k) = (12j)(1k2)$.

We now show that the alternating groups $A_n, n \neq 4$, are simple groups. Clearly, A_2 and A_3 are simple, since $A_2 = \{(1)\}$ and A_3 has prime order. That A_4 is not a simple group has already been discussed (Example 27). Thus it remains to prove that A_n is simple for $n > 4$. For this we need the following theorem.

Theorem 31   Let H be a normal subgroup of $A_n, n > 3$. If H contains a cycle of length 3, then $H = A_n$.

Proof: We may denote the cycle by (123). Now H normal implies that $P^{-1}(123)P$ belongs to H for all permutations P in A_n. In particular, $(23k)^{-1} \times (123)(23k) = (1k2)$ belongs to H for $k > 3$. Now $(1k2)$ in H implies $(1k2) \times (1k2) = (12k)$ is in H. But the cycles $(12k)$ generate A_n, and so we have $H = A_n$.

Theorem 32 A_n is a simple group for $n > 4$.

Proof: Let $H \neq \{(1)\}$ be a normal subgroup of A_n. We must show that $H = A_n$. Let P be an element of H. Now P may be written as a product of disjoint cycles, say $P = P_1 P_2 \cdots P_s$. Suppose at least one of these cycles, say P_1, has length greater than 3. Then we may write $P = (123 \ldots m) P_2 P_3 \cdots P_s$. Consider the permutation $Q = (132)$. H normal in A_n implies that H contains $(123) P (132)$. Since (132) commutes with $P_2 P_3 \cdots P_s$ (why?), $(123) P (132) = (123)(123 \ldots m)(132) P_2 P_3 \cdots P_s = (14 \ldots m23) P_2 P_3 \cdots P_s$. It follows that H contains $(14 \ldots m23) P_2 P_3 \cdots P_s P^{-1} = (14 \ldots m23)(m \ldots 321) = (124)$. Thus $H = A_n$ by Theorem 31.

It remains to reach the conclusion when every element of H is a product of cycles of length 2 or 3. If we suppose that two of the cycles of P, say P_1 and P_2, have length 3, then we may write $P = (123)(456) P_3 \cdots P_s$. Consider $Q = (354)$. Now $(345) P (354) = (345)(123)(456)(354) P_3 \cdots P_s = (124)(365) P_3 \cdots P_s$ belongs to H, as does $(124)(365) P_3 \cdots P_s P^{-1} = (16345)$; a contradiction.

When P has only one cycle of length 3, say $P_1 = (123)$, then (132) belongs to H where $(132) = (123) P_2 \cdots P_s (123) P_2 \cdots P_s$. Again, $H = A_n$ by Theorem 31.

Finally, suppose P is a product of transpositions. Then we may write $P = (12)(34) P_3 \cdots P_s$. Let $Q = (142)$. Then $(124) P (142) = (13)(24) P_3 \cdots P_s$ belongs to H, which implies that $(13)(24) P_3 \cdots P_s P^{-1} = (14)(23)$ belongs to H. Now consider $R = (235)$. Since $(253)(14)(23)(235) = (14)(25)$, and $(14)(25) \times (23)(14) = (235)$, (235) is an element of H. Therefore $H = A_n$ and the proof is completed.

Remark 20 The only subgroup H of S_n, $n > 4$, such that $[S_n : H] = 2$, is A_n. For suppose $[S_n : H] = 2$. Then H is normal in S_n, implying that $H \cap A_n$ is normal in A_n. Now A_n is simple for $n > 4$. Thus $H \cap A_n = \{(1)\}$ or A_n. Clearly, $H \cap A_n = A_n$. This implies that $A_n \subseteq H$. Since $[S_n : A_n] = 2$, we have $A_n = H$. (Is this result also true for $n \leq 4$?)

2-3. COMPOSITION SERIES SOLVABLE GROUPS

At this time we will prove the well-known Jordan-Hölder theorem for composition series and develop some useful results on solvable groups.

Definition 27 A finite sequence $\{e\} = H_0 \subseteq H_1 \subseteq H_2 \subseteq \cdots \subseteq H_r = G$ of subgroups of a group G is called a *normal series* if H_{i-1} is normal in H_i, $i = 1, 2, \ldots, r$. The factor groups H_i / H_{i-1} are called the *factors* of the normal series.

Note: In a normal series, a term may be repeated any number of times. If this is not the case, we speak of a series without repetitions.

Definition 28 A second normal series $\{e\} = K_0 \subseteq K_1 \subseteq K_2 \subseteq \cdots \subseteq K_s = G$ is called a *refinement* of the first one if all the H_i also occur in this second series.

Definition 29   Two normal series are called *isomorphic* if all factors of one series are isomorphic with the factors of the second series in some order.

Definition 30   A normal series without repetitions, which cannot be refined without repetition, is called a *composition series*. The factors of a composition series are called *composition factors*.

Remark 21   A normal series $\{e\} = H_0 \subset H_1 \subset \cdots \subset H_r = G$ is a composition series if, and only if, H_{i-1} is a maximal normal subgroup of H_i for each i. That is, if, and only if, H_i/H_{i-1} is simple for each i.

Remark 22   Every finite group G possesses at least one composition series.

Proof: If G is simple, $\{e\} \subseteq G$ is a composition series. Suppose G is not simple.   Then G contains a proper normal subgroup (and therefore a proper maximal normal subgroup), say K_{r-1}. Now $\{e\} \subset K_{r-1} \subset G$ is a composition series if K_{r-1} is simple. If K_{r-1} is not simple, then $K_{r-1} \supset K_{r-2}$ where K_{r-2} is a maximal normal subgroup of K_{r-1}. $\{e\} \subset K_{r-2} \subset K_{r-1} \subset G$ is a composition series if K_{r-2} is simple. If K_{r-2} is not simple, we continue as above, arriving at a composition series $\{e\} \subset K_1 \subset K_2 \subset \cdots \subset K_{r-1} \subset G$. The finiteness of G implies that there is only a finite number of the K_i. (Each K_{i-1} is a maximal normal subgroup of K_i.)

Exercise 38   Prove that if G is an infinite cyclic group, G does not possess a composition series.

Example 28   The cyclic group G of order 20 generated by a has the following normal subgroups: $\{e\}$, $H_1 = \{a^{10}, e\}$, $H_2 = \{a^5, a^{10}, a^{15}, e\}$, $H_3 = \{a^4, a^8, a^{12}, a^{16}, e\}$, $H_4 = \{a^2, a^4, \ldots, a^{18}, e\}$, and $G = \{a, a^2, \ldots, a^{19}, e\}$. $\{e\} \subset H_3 \subset H_4 \subset G$, $\{e\} \subset H_1 \subset H_4 \subset G$, and $\{e\} \subset H_1 \subset H_2 \subset G$ are composition series for G. The composition factors for $\{e\} \subset H_3 \subset H_4 \subset G$ are $G/H_4 = \{H_4, H_4a\}$, $H/H_3 = \{H_3, H_3a^2\}$, and $H_3/\{e\} = H_3$. The factors of $\{e\} \subset H_1 \subset H_2 \subset G$ are $G/H_2 = \{H_2, H_2a, H_2a^2, H_2a^3, H_2a^4\}$, $H_2/H_1, = \{H_1, H_1a^5\}$, and $H_1/\{e\} = H_1$.

Now consider the following mappings: $\pi_1 \colon G/H_4 \to H_2/H_1$ defined by $\pi_1(H_4) = H_1$, $\pi_1(H_4a) = H_1a^5$; $\pi_2 \colon H_4/H_3 \to H_1$ defined by $\pi_2(H_3) = e$, $\pi_2(H_3a^2) = a^{10}$; $\pi_3 \colon H_3 \to G/H_2$ defined by $\pi_3(e) = H_2$, $\pi_3(a^i) = H_2a^i$, $i = 1, 2, 3, 4$. π_1, π_2, and π_3 are isomorphisms.

Thus it appears that a group G may have more than one composition series, but when this is the case, they have the same length and the composition factors of one are isomorphic to the composition factors of the other. This is the Jordan-Hölder theorem, which we prove after first considering the following:

Theorem 33   Suppose G is a group, H and K distinct maximal normal subgroups of G. Then G/H is isomorphic to $K/H \cap K$ and G/K is isomorphic to $H/H \cap K$.

Proof: We first note that $H \cap K$ is normal in H and in K (Exercise 15). Now HK is a normal subgroup of G (Exercise 18). Since H and K are distinct, we have $H \subset HK \subseteq G$. The fact that H is a maximal normal subgroup of G implies that HK must be G.

Let $D = H \cap K$ and decompose K according to cosets of D, obtaining $K = D + Dx_2 + Dx_3 + \cdots$. Then $HK = HD + (HD)x_2 + (HD)x_3 + \cdots$. (For suppose hk belongs to HK. Now k belongs to K, and so k belongs to Dx_i for some i. Thus hk is an element of $(HD)x_i$, which implies that $HK \subseteq HD + (HD)x_2 + \cdots$. But $HK = G$ implies $HK \supseteq HD + (HD)x_2 + \cdots$.) Since $HD = H$ ($H \cap K \subseteq H$), we have $G = H + Hx_2 + Hx_3 + \cdots$. This is a decomposition of G according to cosets of H, since if $Hx_i = Hx_j$, then $hx_i = h'x_j$, implying that $x_i x_j^{-1} = h^{-1}h'$ is in H. Now x_i and x_j belong to K. Thus $x_i x_j^{-1}$ belongs to K. Hence we have $x_i x_j^{-1}$ in D and so $Dx_i = Dx_j$; a contradiction. ($D + Dx_2 + Dx_3 + \cdots$ is a decomposition of K.)

Now $G/H = \{H, Hx_2, Hx_3, \dots\}$ and $K/D = \{D, Dx_2, Dx_3, \dots\}$. Let π: $G/H \to K/D$ be defined by $\pi(Hx_i) = Dx_i$, $i = 1, 2, \dots$. ($Hx_1 = H$; $Dx_1 = D$.) Clearly, π is 1-1 and onto. Since $\pi(Hx_i Hx_j) = \pi(Hx_i Hx_j) = Dx_i x_j = Dx_i Dx_j = \pi(Hx_i)\pi(Hx_j)$, π is an isomorphism. That G/K is isomorphic to H/D is left as an exercise.

Note: In some of the material which follows we shall find it convenient to change our notation for denoting a series. For example, we may write $G = H_0 \supset H_1 \supset \cdots \supset H_r = \{e\}$ instead of $\{e\} = H_0 \subset H_1 \subset \cdots \subset H_r = G$.

Theorem 34 (Jordon-Hölder) Let $G \neq \{e\}$ be a finite group with two composition series

$$G = H_0 \supset H_1 \supset \cdots \supset H_r = \{e\},$$
$$G = K_0 \supset K_1 \supset \cdots \supset K_s = \{e\}.$$

Then $r = s$ and the factor groups H_{i-1}/H_i are isomorphic with the factor groups K_{j-1}/K_j in some order.

Proof: Let G have order $n = p_1 p_2 \cdots p_t$ (where the p_i are primes, not necessarily distinct). The proof will be by induction on t. For $t = 1$, G is a group of prime order, and thus has no proper subgroups. Therefore $G \supset \{e\}$ is the only composition series. Suppose the theorem true for $t = 1, 2, \dots, k$ and let G be a group whose order contains $k + 1$ prime factors. If G is simple, then $G \supset \{e\}$ is again the only composition series. If G is not simple, there is a composition series of length greater than 1. (By "length" we mean the number of composition factors.) If this series is unique there is nothing to prove. If it is not unique then there exists two distinct composition series of length greater than 1, say

$$(*) \quad G = H_0 \supset H_1 \supset \cdots \supset H_u = e \ , \text{ and}$$
$$(**) \quad G = K_0 \supset K_1 \supset \cdots \supset K_v = e \ .$$

If $H_1 = K_1$, the theorem follows by the induction hypothesis. (The order of H_1 contains k or fewer prime factors.) If $H_1 \neq K_1$, we let $D = H_1 \cap K_1$ and consider

(i) $G \supset H_1 \supset D \supset D_1 \supset \cdots \supset Dw = e \ ,$

(ii) $G \supset K_1 \supset D \supset D_1 \supset \cdots \supset Dw = e \ ,$

where $D \supset D_1 \supset \cdots \supset D_w$ is a composition series for D. Since H_1 is a maximal normal subgroup in G, G/H_1 is simple. Since G/H_1 is isomorphic to K_1/D (Theorem 33), K_1/D is simple, and thus D is a maximal normal subgroup in K_1. Hence (i) and (ii) are two composition series. Since G/H_1 is isomorphic to K_1/D and H_1/D is isomorphic to G/K_1, and the order of D contains fewer than k prime factors, the theorem holds for the series (i) and (ii). Since G/H_1 is isomorphic to G/H_1, and the order of H_1 contains k or fewer prime factors, the theorem holds for the series $(*)$ and (i). Similarly, the theorem holds for the series $(**)$ and (ii). It follows that the theorem is true for the composition series $(*)$ and $(**)$. This completes the proof.

Definition 31 A group G is said to be solvable (soluble) if the sequence $G \supseteq G' \supseteq G'' \supseteq \ldots$,where each group $G^{(i)}$ is the derived group (see Exercise 20) of the preceding, terminates in the identity subgroup in a finite number of steps, say $G^{(s)} = \{e\}$.

Note: If $G^{(i)} = G^{(i+1)}$, then $G^{(i)} = G^{(j)}$ for all $j > i$.

Exercise 39 Prove that every subgroup of a solvable group is solvable.

Theorem 35 A group G of finite order is solvable if, and only if, the factor groups in any composition series for G are cyclic of prime order.

Proof: Let $G = H_0 \supset H_1 \supset \cdots \supset H_r = \{e\}$ be a composition series where each H_{i-1}/H_i is cyclic of some prime order. Since G/H_1 is Abelian, $H_1 \supseteq G'$ (Exercise 27). Since H_1/H_2 is Abelian, and since $H_1' \supseteq G''$, we have $H_2 \supseteq H_1' \supseteq G''$. It follows that $H_r \supseteq G^{(r)}$. Thus $G^{(r)} = \{e\}$, implying that G is solvable. Conversely, suppose G is a finite solvable group with $G \supset G' \supset G'' \supset \cdots \supset G^{(s)} = \{e\}$. Let H_1 be a maximal normal subgroup of G such that $H_1 \supseteq G'$. Now G/H_1 is simple (Remark 19). Since G/G' is Abelian and $G/G' \supseteq G/H_1$, G/H_1 is also Abelian. Thus G/H_1 is cyclic of prime order (Exercise 36). Let H_2 be a maximal normal subgroup in H_1. Since H_1 is solvable (Exercise 39), H_1/H_2 is cyclic of prime order. Continuing, we have a composition series $G = H_0 \supset H_1 \supset H_2 \supset \cdots \supset H_r = \{e\}$ with each H_{i-1}/H_i cyclic of prime order. Thus the factors in any composition series will be cyclic of prime order by the Jordan-Hölder theorem.

Theorem 36 G is solvable if, and only if, G has a finite normal series $G = H_0 \supseteq H_1 \supseteq H_2 \supseteq \cdots \supseteq H_s = \{e\}$ in which every factor H_{i-1}/H_i is Abelian.

Proof: This is clear if G is solvable. Suppose $G = H_0 \supseteq H_1 \supseteq \cdots \supseteq H_s = \{e\}$ is a normal series in which each H_{i-1}/H_i is Abelian. Then $H_1 \supseteq G'$. Similarly, H_2 normal in H_1 and H_1/H_2 Abelian imply that $H_2 \supseteq H_1' (\supseteq G'')$ since $H_1 \supseteq G'$). Finally, we have $\{e\} = H_s \supseteq G^{(s)}$, implying that $G^{(s)} = \{e\}$, which in turn implies that G is solvable.

Example 29 Every Abelian group G is solvable, since in this case we have $G' = \{e\}$.

Example 30 The symmetric groups S_n for $n \leqslant 4$ are solvable. In S_3, $S_3 \supset A_3 \supset \{e\}$ is the only composition series. The factors S_3/A_3 and $A_3/\{e\}$ have order 2 and 3 respectively. $\{e\} \subset K \subset N \subset A_4 \subset S_4$ where $N = \{P_1, P_2, P_3, P_4\}$ and $K = \{P_1, P_2\}$, is a composition series for S_4. Here, $|S_4/A_4| = 2$, $|A_4/N| = 3$, $|N/K| = 2$, and $|K/\{e\}| = 2$.

Remark 23 It can be shown (see Chapter 5) that the general nth degree equation is solvable by radicals (that is, by using rational operations and extraction of roots) if, and only if, the symmetric group S_n is a solvable group. Thus there exist formulas (such as the quadratic formula) that give the general solution to equations of degree $n \leqslant 4$. That no such formulas exist for equations of degree $n \geqslant 5$ (that is, such equations are not solvable by radicals) is evident when one observes that S_n for $n \geqslant 5$ is not solvable. This is immediate from the fact that the only composition series for such a symmetric group is $S_n \supset A_n \supset \{e\}$. Now S_n/A_n has prime order, but $A_n/\{e\}$ does not. $|A_n/\{e\}| = \dfrac{n!}{2}$, which is not a prime for $n > 4$.

Exercise 40 Every quotient group of a solvable group is solvable.

Exercise 41 Prove that if a group G contains a subgroup H with the property that H and G/H are both solvable groups, then G must also be solvable.

2-4. DIRECT PRODUCTS

We conclude this chapter with some results on direct products of groups.

Definition 32 Let H and K be groups. The set $H \times K = \{(h,k); h \text{ in } H, k \text{ in } K\}$ is called the *direct product* of H and K.

Suppose we define a binary operation $*$ in $H \times K$ as follows: $(h,k) * (h',k') = (hh',kk')$. Then $H \times K$ together with $*$ is a group. For suppose $(h_1, k_1), (h_2, k_2)$, and (h_3,k_3) are elements of the direct product $H \times K$. Then $[(h_1,k_1)(h_2,k_2)] \times (h_3,k_3) = (h_1\ h_2,\ k_1\ k_2)(h_3,\ k_3) = ((h_1\ h_2)h_3,\ (k_1\ k_2)k_3) = (h_1(h_2\ h_3),\ k_1(k_2\ k_3)) = (h_1,k_1)(h_2h_3,k_2\ k_3) = (h_1,k_1)\ [(h_2,k_2)(h_3,k_3)]$, and $*$ is associative. If e and e' denote the identities of H and K respectively, then (e,e') is the identity of $H \times K$. Finally, $(h,k)^{-1} = (h^{-1},k^{-1})$.

Note: One can of course generalize Definition 32 to the direct product of three or more groups. We shall, however, limit our discussion here to the direct product of two groups.

Exercise 42 Suppose H is a cyclic group of order m and K a cyclic group of order n, where m and n are relatively prime. Show that $H \times K$ is cyclic of order mn.

Remark 24 $H \times K$ contains a subgroup isomorphic to H and a subgroup isomorphic to K.

Proof: Let $H_1 = \{(h,e');\ h$ in H, e' the identity of $K\}$ and $K_1 = \{(e,k);\ e$ the identity of H, k in $K\}$. Clearly, H_1 and K_1 are subgroups of $H \times K$. Define $\pi_1: H_1 \to H$ by $\pi_1((h,e')) = h$. It is clear that π_1 is 1-1 and onto. Since $\pi_1((h,e')(h',e')) = \pi_1((hh',e')) = hh' = \pi_1((h,e'))\pi_1((h',e'))$, π_1 is an isomorphism. Similarly, $\pi_2 : K_1 \to K$ defined by $\pi_2((e,k)) = k$, is an isomorphism of K_1 onto K.

We may write $H_1 = H \times \{e'\}$ and $K_1 = \{e\} \times K$. Since π_1 and π_2 are isomorphisms, we identify H with $H \times \{e'\}$ and K with $\{e\} \times K$.

Exercise 43 Prove that $(H \times K)/H$ is isomorphic to K and $(H \times K)/K$ is isomorphic to H.

We have seen that given two arbitrary groups H and K, we can form a group $H \times K$, the direct product of H and K. We turn our attention now to the following: suppose G is a group and H and K subgroups of G. When will G be the direct product of H and K? (More precisely, we want to know when G will be isomorphic to the direct product $H \times K$, since clearly G can never actually equal this product.)

Theorem 37 Let G be a group, H and K subgroups of G. If
   (i) every element of H commutes with every element of K, and
   (ii) every element g in G can be uniquely expressed in the form $g = hk$, h in H, k in K, then
   (a) $H \cap K = \{e\}$, and
   (b) G is isomorphic to $H \times K$.
   Proof: Suppose x is an element of $H \cap K$. Then x^{-1} belongs to $H \cap K$ (since $H \cap K$ is a subgroup). Let g belong to G. Now $g = hk$ and $g = (hx) \times (x^{-1}k)$ are two representations of g as a product of an element in H by an

element in K. Thus by (ii) we have $hx = h$ and $x^{-1}k = k$, which implies that $x = e$. Therefore $H \cap K = \{e\}$.

To prove (b), let g belong to G. Then $g = hk$, h in H, k in K (and this representation of g is unique). Consider $\pi: G \to H \times K$ defined by $\pi(g) = (h,k)$. Clearly, π is onto. Also $(h,k) = (h',k')$ implies that $h = h'$ and $k = k'$, which implies that $hk = h'k'$, which implies that π is 1-1. Suppose $g_1 = h_1 k_1$ and $g_2 = h_2 k_2$. Then $\pi(g_1 g_2) = \pi(h_1 k_1 h_2 k_2) = \pi(h_1 h_2 k_1 k_2)$, (by (i)), $= (h_1 h_2, k_1 k_2) = (h_1,k_1)(h_2,k_2) = \pi(g_1)\pi(g_2)$. Therefore π is an isomorphism and G is isomorphic to $H \times K$.

Thus (i) and (ii) above are enough to insure that G be isomorphic to the direct product of its subgroups H and K. Conversely, if $G = H \times K$, then (i) and (ii) hold, as well as (a). We prove this now.

Theorem 38 Let G be a group, H and K subgroups of G. If G is isomorphic to $H \times K$, then (in $H \times K$)

(i) every element of H commutes with every element of K,

(ii) every element g in G can be expressed uniquely in the form $g = hk$, h in H, k in K, and

(iii) $H \cap K = \{e\}$.

Proof: We identify H with $H \times \{e\}$ and K with $\{e\} \times K$. Since $(h,e) \times (e,k) = (h,k) = (e,k)(h,e)$, (i) holds. Let g belong to G. Then $g = (h,k) = (h, e) \times (e,k)$ is an element of $(H \times \{e\})(\{e\} \times K)$, which is isomorphic to HK. Thus there is at least one representation of g of the required form. Suppose $g = (h,e)(e,k)$ and $g = (h',e)(e,k')$. Then $(h,e)(e,k) = (h',e)(e,k')$, which implies that $(h,k) = (h',k')$. Thus $h = h'$ and $k = k'$, and there is at most one such representation. Therefore (ii) holds. Finally, suppose x belongs to $H \cap K$. Then x is in H and x is in K. Thus $x = (h,e)$ and $x = (e,k)$. Therefore $h = e$ and $k = e$, implying that $H \cap K = \{(e,e)\} = \{e\}$. Hence (iii) holds.

Remark 25 If H and K are normal subgroups of a group G such that $H \cap K = \{e\}$, then every element of H commutes with every element of K.

Proof: Suppose h belongs to H and k belongs to K. Then $h^{-1}k^{-1}hk = h^{-1}(k^{-1}hk)$ belongs to $H(h$ in H implies h^{-1} in H; $H \triangle G$ implies $k^{-1}hk$ is in H) and $h^{-1}k^{-1}hk = (h^{-1}k^{-1}h)k$ belongs to K (k in K implies k^{-1} in K; $K \triangle G$ implies $h^{-1}k^{-1}h$ is in K). Therefore $h^{-1}k^{-1}hk$ belongs to $H \cap K$. Since $H \cap K = \{e\}$, we have $h^{-1}k^{-1}hk = e$. Thus $hk = kh$.

It follows from Remark 25 that we may replace Theorem 37 by the following:

Theorem 37′ Let G be a group, H and K subgroups of G. If

(i) H is normal in G and K is normal in G,

(ii) every element g in G can be uniquely expressed in the form $g = hk$, h in H, k in K, and

(iii) $H \cap K = e$, then G is isomorphic to $H \times K$.

From the proof of Exercise 43, we see that H and K are normal in $H \times K$. Thus Theorem 38 may be replaced by the following, which is the converse of Theorem 37'.

Theorem 38'   Let G be a group, H and K subgroups of G. If G is isomorphic to $H \times K$, then

(i) H and K are normal in G,

(ii) every element g in G can be uniquely expressed in the form $g = hk$, h in H, k in K, and

(iii) $H \cap K = \{e\}$.

Example 31   Suppose H is the multiplicative group of positive real numbers and K the cyclic group of order 2 generated by -1 with respect to multiplication. Then G, the multiplicative group of nonzero real numbers, is isomorphic to $H \times K$ under the mapping π defined as follows: $\pi(g) = (g,1)$, g positive, and $\pi(g) = (|g|, -1)$, g negative.

Example 32   The group G of Example 11 is the direct product of its subgroups $H = \{1, 10\}$ and $K = \{1, 3, 4, 5, 9\}$.

Example 33   Consider the subgroups $K_1 = \{I, H\}$ and $K_2 = \{I, R, R', R''\}$ of the group $G = \{I, R, R', R'', H, V, D, D'\}$ of symmetries of the square. Clearly, $K_1 \cap K_2 = \{I\}$. Also, $G = K_1 K_2$, as is evident from Table 1. Thus (ii) and (iii) of Theorem 37' hold. Now $K_1 \times K_2 = \{(I,I), (I,R), (I,R'), (I,R''), (H,I), (H,R), (H,R'), (H,R'')\}$. Since G contains 5 elements of order 2, while $K_1 \times K_2$ contains only 3, there can be no isomorphism of G onto the direct product of its subgroups K_1 and K_2. Therefore one of the subgroups, K_1 or K_2, must not be normal in G. (Which one?)

Exercise 44   Show that the group of symmetries of the square is not isomorphic to a direct product of any of its proper subgroups.

Exercise 45   Prove or disprove: A direct product of solvable groups is solvable.

3

p-Groups

3-1. CONVERSE OF LAGRANGE'S THEOREM
DOUBLE COSETS

We have seen that the order of a subgroup of a finite group must be a divisor of the order of the group (Theorem 7). The converse of this, however, is not generally true. For example, the reader can show that the alternating group A_4, although containing subgroups of order 2, 3, and 4, does not have any subgroup of order 6.

Of interest to us now is determining when a group of order n will contain a subgroup of order m, m a divisor of n. You will recall that we have already discussed this for cyclic groups (Remark 12).

Theorem 39 Suppose G is an Abelian group of order n. If n is divisible by p, a prime, then G contains an element of order p (and thus a subgroup of order p).

Proof: Suppose $n = mp$ and proceed by induction on m. For $m = 1$ the theorem is clear. If $m \neq 1$, G contains proper subgroups (Theorem 10). Let H be a proper subgroup having maximal order, say h. There are two cases:

(i) p divides h. By the induction hypothesis H contains an element $x \neq e$ such that $x^p = e$. But x belongs to G.

(ii) p does not divide h (that is, p and h are relatively prime). Since $H \subset G$, there exists an element x not in H. Let the order of x be k, and K be the cyclic subgroup generated by x. Consider HK. Now G is Abelian, which implies that $HK = KH$. Thus HK is a subgroup of G (Exercise 16). Clearly, $HK \supset H$. Since H was assumed to be a proper subgroup having maximal order, it follows that $HK = G$. Now the order of HK is $\dfrac{hk}{d}$, where d is the order of $H \cap K$ (Theorem 15). Thus $nd = hk$. Since

p divides nd, and since $(p,h) = 1$, we have p divides k. Let $k = ps$. Then the element $y = x^s$ has order p.

Theorem 39 is also true when G is non-Abelian, as we now show.

Theorem 40   Suppose G is a group of order n. If n is divisible by a prime p, then G contains an element of order p.

Proof: As in the proof of Theorem 39, we let $n = mp$ and proceed by induction on m. The theorem is clear if $m = 1$. If $m \neq 1$, then G will contain at least one proper subgroup. Again we distinguish two cases:

   (i) G contains a proper subgroup H such that $[G:H]$ is not divisible by p. Then p divides the order of H, and by the induction hypothesis H (and hence G) contains an element of order p.

   (ii) If H is a proper subgroup of G, then $[G:H]$ is divisible by p. From Exercise 28, $n = n_1 + n_2 + \cdots + n_s$, where each n_i is the number of conjugates in a class of elements of G. If $n_i \neq 1$, then n_i must be the index of a proper subgroup, and hence divisible by p. Now $n_1 = 1$ (the identity e is a class). Therefore, the number of $n_i = 1$ is a multiple of p. Since an element a_i is a class in G if, and only if, it is in the center of G, the order of $Z(G)$ is divisible by p. Since $Z(G)$ is Abelian, $Z(G)$ contains an element x of order p (this is Theorem 39). Of course, x belongs to G.

Let G be a group of order n. Now we may write n as a product of primes, say $n = p_1 p_2 \cdots p_s$. Of course, the p_i need not all be distinct. If this be the case, then the order of G is divisible by some power of a prime, say p^i. Theorem 40 guarantees the existence of a subgroup of G having order p, but not of order p^i. We shall show shortly, however, that when G has order divisible by a prime power, then G has a subgroup of this prime power order.

In Sec. 1-2 the concept of coset was introduced. We shall now extend this to the concept of double coset. (In making use of double cosets, our approach is founded on the treatment given by Marshall Hall Jr. in his *The Theory of Groups* (New York: Macmillan, 1959).)

Definition 33   Let G be a group, H and K subgroups of G (not necessarily distinct). The set $HxK = \{ hxk; h$ in H, k in K, x a fixed element of $G \}$ is called a *double coset*.

Exercise 46   Prove that two double cosets HxK and HyK are either disjoint or identical.

   Note: A double coset HxK contains all right cosets of H of the form Hxk, k in K, and all left cosets of K of the form hxK, h in H.

Theorem 41   The number of left cosets of K in HxK is the index of $K \cap x^{-1}Hx$

in $x^{-1}Hx$ (that is, $[x^{-1}Hx:K \cap x^{-1}Hx]$) and the number of right cosets of H in HxK is the index of $K \cap x^{-1}Hx$ in K (that is, $[K:K \cap x^{-1}Hx]$).

Proof: Let $x^{-1}Hx = A$ and $K \cap A = D$. We decompose A according to left cosets of D such that $A = D + u_2D + \cdots + u_rD$, where $[A:D] = r$. Then K, u_2K, $\ldots, u_rK$ are left cosets of K in AK. (The reader should show that these cosets are distinct.) Now every left coset of K in AK has the form aK, a in A, where $a = u_id$, d in D. But $u_idK = u_iK$. Thus the number of left cosets of K in AK is equal to the index of D in A; that is, $[x^{-1}Hx:K \cap x^{-1}Hx]$. Since the 1-1 mapping $f:HxK \to x^{-1}HxK$ defined by $f(hxk) = x^{-1}hxk$, is also a 1-1 mapping of the set of left cosets of K in HxK onto the set of left cosets of K in $x^{-1}HxK$, it follows that $[x^{-1}Hx:K \cap x^{-1}Hx]$ is the number of left cosets of K in HxK. Similarly we may show that the number of right cosets of A in AK is equal to the index of D in K; that is, $[K:K \cap x^{-1}Hx]$. But this is the number of right cosets of H in HxK since f is also a 1-1 mapping of the set of right cosets of H in HxK onto the set of right cosets of $x^{-1}Hx$ in $x^{-1}HxK$.

Example 34 In S_4, let $H = \{P_1, P_5, P_6, P_{16}, P_{22}, P_{24}\}$, $K = \{P_1, P_2, P_3, P_4, P_{18}, P_{19}, P_{22}, P_{23}\}$, and $x = P_8$. Then $HxK = S_4$, $x^{-1}Hx = \{P_1, P_9, P_{10}, P_{13}, P_{21}, P_{22}\}$, and $K \cap x^{-1}Hx = \{P_1, P_{22}\}$. Clearly, there are 3 distinct left cosets of K in HxK and 4 distinct right cosets of H in HxK. It is also clear that $[x^{-1}Hx:K \cap x^{-1}Hx] = 3$ and $[K:K \cap x^{-1}Hx] = 4$.

Theorem 42 Suppose G is a group of order $n = p^m s$, where p is a prime and $(p,s) = 1$. Then G contains at least one subgroup of order p^i, $i = 1, 2, \ldots, m$. Furthermore, each subgroup of order p^i, $i = 1, 2, \ldots, m-1$, is normal in at least one subgroup of order p^{i+1}.

Proof: Since G contains a subgroup of order p (Theorem 40) we may proceed by induction on i. Let H be a subgroup of G having order p^i, where $1 \leqslant i < m$, and decompose G according to double cosets of H obtaining $G = H + Hx_2H + \cdots + Hx_rH$. Let n_j be the number of left cosets of H in Hx_jH. Then $n_j = [x_j^{-1}Hx_j:H \cap x_j^{-1}Hx_j]$ by Theorem 41. Now $[G:H] = n_1 + n_2 + \cdots + n_r$. Also, each n_j is 1 or a power of p (note that $n_1 = 1$ since $x_1 = e$). Since p divides $[G:H]$, the number of n_j's equal to 1 must be a multiple of p. For $n_j = 1$ we have $x_j^{-1}Hx_j = H$, which implies that x_j belongs to $N_G(H)$. And for x_j in $N_G(H)$, we have $x_j^{-1}Hx_j = H$, and so $n_j = 1$. Hence the number of n_j's equal to 1 is $[N_G(H):H]$, and the order of $N_G(H)/H$ is divisible by p. Thus $N_G(H)/H$ contains a subgroup K' of order p (Theorem 40). It follows from Theorem 23 that $K' = K/H$ where $H \subseteq K \subseteq N_G(H)$, and $[K:H] = [K':\{e\}] = p$. Hence, K is a subgroup of order p^{i+1} and $H \triangle K$.

It is to be emphasized in Theorem 42 that the subgroups of G of order p^m

need *not* necessarily be normal in G. S_4 has order $24 = 2^3 \cdot 3$, and thus must contain at least one subgroup of order 8. We have seen (Example 34) that $K = \{P_1, P_2, P_3, P_4, P_{18}, P_{19}, P_{22}, P_{23}\}$ is such a subgroup. Yet, since $P_7^{-1} P_{18} P_7 = P_{17}$ is not an element of K, K is not a normal subgroup of S_4.

Exercise 47   Show that no subgroup of order 8 in S_4 is normal.

3-2.   P-GROUPS

Theorem 42 gives us a good deal of information about the subgroups of any finite group G, since the order of any finite group can be expressed in the form $p^m s$, p a prime, $(p,s) = 1$. Of particular interest is the case where $s = 1$. Here, G is a group of prime power order. These are the *p*-groups.

Definition 34   A group G is called a *p-group* if it has order a power of the prime p.

Note: Clearly, if G is a *p*-group, then every element of G has order a power of p. If G is a finite group such that every element of G has order a power of p, then G itself has order a power of p (the order of G cannot be divisible by two different primes), and thus is a *p*-group.

Remark 26   All *p*-groups are solvable.

Proof: If G is a group of order p^m, then G contains a normal subgroup H_{m-1} of order p^{m-1} (Theorem 42). H_{m-1} contains a normal subgroup H_{m-2} of order p^{m-2}. By a continued application of Theorem 42 we have a composition series $\{e\} = H_0 \subset H_1 \subset \cdots \subset H_{m-1} \subset G$, where clearly, each composition factor has prime order. Thus G is solvable by Theorem 35.

Theorem 43   If G is a *p*-group $(G \neq \{e\})$, then $Z(G) \neq \{e\}$. (That is, the center of a *p*-group $\neq \{e\}$ has order at least p.)

Proof: We have $G = C_1 + C_2 + \cdots + C_r$ where each C_i is a class of conjugate elements (Exercise 28). Let n_i be the number of elements in C_i. From Theorem 16, n_i is the index of a subgroup of G. Thus $n_i = 1$ or is a power of p. If G has order p^m then $p^m = n_1 + n_2 + \cdots + n_r$. Since $n_1 = 1$ (we let $C_1 = \{e\}$), it follows that the remaining n_i's are not all powers of p. Thus $n_i = 1$ for at least one $i > 1$, and so $Z(G)$ contains elements other than e. (An element in $Z(G)$ forms a class by itself.)

Theorem 44   Suppose G is a *p*-group and N a normal subgroup of G of order p. Then $N \subseteq Z(G)$.

Proof: Let a be a generator of N. Then $N = \{a, a^2, \ldots, a^{p-1}, e\}$. From Theorem 16 we have that the number of conjugates of a is $[G : N_G(a)]$, and thus is 1 or a power of p. Since a has at most $p-1$ conjugates (the conjugates of a are among the elements $a, a^2, \ldots, a^{p-1}$, since N is a normal subgroup), the only conjugate of a is a itself. Thus a (and therefore N) is contained in $Z(G)$.

Example 35   It has already been noted (Example 22) that the center of the group G of symmetries of the square is $K_4 = \{I, R'\}$. Thus, in this non-Abelian p-group G, the order of the center is p. It follows from Theorem 44 that K_4 is the only normal subgroup of G having order p. (See Example 24.)

It will be an immediate consequence of Theorem 46 that the center of any non-Abelian p-group G of order p^3 is always of order p. The center can be the only normal subgroup of G having order p by Theorem 44.

Theorem 45   Let G be a group and N a normal subgroup of G. If $N \subseteq Z(\mathbf{G})$ and G/N is cyclic, then G is Abelian.

   Proof: Suppose G/N is generated by the coset Na. Since every element of G is in some coset of N, we may express the elements of G in the form $g = na^i$, where n is in the center of G. For $g_1 = n_1 a^i$ and $g_2 = n_2 a^j$, we have $g_1 g_2 = n_1 a^i n_2 a^j = n_1 n_2 a^{i+j} = n_2 n_1 a^{j+i} = n_2 a^j n_1 a^i = g_2 g_1$. Thus G is an Abelian group.

Remark 27   It follows from Theorem 45 that if G is a non-Abelian group, the only possible cyclic quotient groups G/N of G are the quotient groups by normal subgroups N such that N is not contained in the center of G. In particular, $G/Z(G)$ is not cyclic if G is not Abelian. (See comment following Example 23.)

Exercise 48   Find the cyclic quotient groups of the alternating group A_4.

   Note: Every homomorphic image of a cyclic group is cyclic (Exercise 25). However, Exercise 48 shows that all homomorphic images of a noncyclic group need not be noncyclic.

Theorem 46   Suppose G is a non-Abelian p-group. Then $[G:Z(G)]$ is divisible by p^2.

   Proof: The quotient group $G/Z(G)$ is not cyclic (Remark 27). Hence the index of $Z(G)$ in G (which is the order of $G/Z(G)$) is not equal to p. Since $[G:Z(G)]$ divides the order of G, a p-group, we have $[G:Z(G)] = p^i, i \geq 2$.

Remark 28   In the above proof we note that G has order p^m, $m \geq 3$, since the order of G is the product of the order of $Z(G)$ and the index of $Z(G)$ in G; and $Z(G)$ has order $p^j, j \geq 1$ by Theorem 43. Thus groups of order p^2 are Abelian.

Remark 29   Suppose G is a non-Abelian group of order p^3. Then $G/Z(G)$ has order p^2. Therefore, by Exercise 27, the derived group G' of G is contained in $Z(G)$. Since $|Z(G)| = p$ and $G' \neq \{e\}$, (since G is non-Abelian) we see that $G' = Z(G)$. That is, in a non-Abelian p-group of order p^3, the center and the derived group are identical.

Exercise 49   Show the existence of two nonisomorphic groups of order p^2 and prove that, to within isomorphism, these are the only groups having order p^2.

3-3.   SYLOW THEOREMS

We have seen that when the order of a group G is divisible by a power of a prime p, then G has a subgroup H of this prime power order. Of course, H is a p-group (p-subgroup of G). Of interest to us now is the case where G is itself not a p-group, but does contain p-subgroups. Of particular interest are the p-subgroups of G having maximal order.

Definition 35   Let G be a group and P a subgroup of G. If P is a p-group, not contained in any larger p-group which is also a subgroup of G, then we call P a *Sylow p-subgroup* of G.

Note: It follows from Theorem 42 that every p-group which is a subgroup of a group G, is contained in a Sylow p-subgroup of G.

Example 36   The Sylow 2-subgroups of S_4 are $H_1 = \{P_1, P_2, P_3, P_4, P_{18}, P_{19}, P_{22}, P_{23}\}$, $H_2 = \{P_1, P_2, P_3, P_4, P_{13}, P_{14}, P_{15}, P_{16}\}$, and $H_3 = \{P_1, P_2, P_3, P_4, P_{17}, P_{20}, P_{21}, P_{24}\}$. For $x_1 = P_5$, $x_2 = P_7$, and $x_3 = P_9$, we have $x_1^{-1}H_1x_1 = H_2$, $x_2^{-1}H_1x_2 = H_3$, and $x_3^{-1}H_2x_3 = H_3$. Thus the Sylow 2-subgroups of S_4 are conjugate. Note that the number of Sylow 2-subgroups is a divisor of the order of S_4.

The Sylow 3-subgroups of S_4 are $K_1 = \{P_1, P_5, P_6\}$, $K_2 = \{P_1, P_{11}, P_{12}\}$, $K_3 = \{P_1, P_9, P_{10}\}$, and $K_4 = \{P_1, P_7, P_8\}$. For $x_4 = P_2, x_5 = P_3, x_6 = P_4, x_7 = P_{16}, x_8 = P_6$, and $x_9 = P_{11}$, we have $x_4^{-1}K_1x_4 = K_2, x_5^{-1}K_1x_5 = K_3, x_6^{-1}K_1x_6 = K_4, x_7^{-1}K_2x_7 = K_3, x_8^{-1}K_2x_8 = K_4$, and $x_9^{-1}K_3x_9 = K_4$. Thus the Sylow 3-subgroups of S_4 are conjugate and the number of Sylow 3-subgroups is a divisor of the order of S_4.

We shall now prove that the above is true in any finite group G. That is, the Sylow p-subgroups of a finite group G are conjugate and the number of Sylow p-subgroups is a divisor of the order of G. In fact, we will show that the number of Sylow p-subgroups has the form $1 + kp$, k an integer.

Theorem 47   The Sylow p-subgroups of a finite group G are conjugate.

Proof: Let P_1 and P_2 be Sylow p-subgroups of G and decompose G according to double cosets, obtaining

$$G = P_1P_2 + P_1x_2P_2 + \cdots + P_1 x_r P_2$$

Let n_j be the number of left cosets of P_2 in $P_1x_jP_2$. Then $n_j = [x_j^{-1}P_1x_j : P_2 \cap x_j^{-1}P_1x_j]$. Now $n_j = 1$, or is a power of p. Since $n_1 + n_2 + \cdots + n_r = [G:P_2]$

is not a multiple of p (else P_2 would be contained in a larger p-group which is a subgroup of G), it follows that $n_j = 1$ for some j. Therefore $x_j^{-1}P_1x_j = P_2$, implying that P_1 and P_2 are conjugate.

Note: The Sylow p-subgroups of G are isomorphic, since they are conjugate.

Exercise 50 Suppose G is a group and P a Sylow p-subgroup of G. Prove that the only Sylow p-subgroup of G that is contained in the normalizer $N_G(P)$ of P, is P.

Theorem 48 In a group G of order n, the number of Sylow p-subgroups is a divisor of n of the form $(1 + kp)$, k an integer.

Proof: Let $P_0, P_1, P_2, \ldots, P_s$ be the Sylow p-subgroups of G. If $s = 0$, the theorem is clear. Suppose $s \neq 0$ and partition $P_1, P_2, \ldots, P_s$ into disjoint conjugate classes with respect to elements of P_0. That is, if there is an element x in P_0 such that $x^{-1}P_ix = P_j$, then P_i and P_j are in the same class. Since P_i is the only Sylow p-subgroup in its normalizer (Exercise 50), it follows that $N_{P_0}(P_i)$, $i \neq 0$, is a proper subgroup of P_0 ($N_{P_0}(P_i) \subseteq N_G(P_i)$). Now the index of $N_{P_0}(P_i)$ in P_0 is the number of conjugates of P_i by elements of P_0 (Theorem 16), and is a power of p. Thus we may write $s = p^{e_1} + p^{e_2} + \cdots + p^{e_t} = kp$, which implies that there are $1 + s = 1 + kp$ Sylow p-subgroups of G. Since the P_i are all conjugate (under G), the number of Sylow p-subgroups is $[G:N_G(P_0)]$. Therefore $1 + kp$ is a divisor of n.

Note: Theorems 42, 47, and 48 are often referred to as the Sylow theorems.

Remark 30 Let G be a group and P a Sylow p-subgroup of G. P is the only Sylow p-subgroup of G if, and only if, P is normal in G.

Proof: Suppose $P \triangle G$. If P' is a Sylow p-subgroup of G, then P and P' are conjugate. Thus, there exists an element x in G such that $x^{-1}Px = P'$. But $x^{-1}Px = P$ for all x in G since P is normal. Thus $P' = P$. Conversely, if P is the only Sylow p-subgroup of G, then $x^{-1}Px = P$ for all x in G, implying that P is normal in G.

Theorem 49 If the Sylow subgroups of a finite group G are normal, then G is the direct product of its Sylow subgroups.

Proof: Suppose G has order $n = p_1^{e_1}p_2^{e_2} \cdots p_s^{e_s}$, p_i prime. There can be only one Sylow p_i-subgroup of G for $i = 1, 2, \ldots, s$ since the Sylow subgroups of G are normal (Remark 30). Let P_i be the Sylow p_i-subgroup of G. Now $P_1P_2 \cdots P_s$ is a subgroup of G (Exercise 18). In fact, $P_1P_2 \cdots P_s = G$ (since P_i has order $p_i^{e_i}$ and $P_i \cap P_j = \{e\}$, $i \neq j$). Thus $G = P_1 \times P_2 \times \cdots \times P_s$ (generalization of Theorem 37').

Remark 31   If the Sylow subgroups of G are normal and cyclic, then G itself must be cyclic (see Exercise 42). Thus we see that there can be but one Abelian group of order $p_1 p_2 \cdots p_s, p_i$ distinct primes; namely the cyclic group of this order.

In Chapter 4 we shall discuss groups of order $p_1 p_2 \cdots p_s, p_i$ prime, in more detail. Of particular interest will be groups of order pq, p and q distinct primes.

It can be shown that there are no simple groups of order $p_1 p_2 \cdots p_s, s > 1$ (p_i distinct primes). We do this here for a group of order 30.

Example 37   Suppose G is a group of order $30 = 2 \cdot 3 \cdot 5$. Now if G is a simple group, then the Sylow subgroups of G are not unique. Thus G has at least 3 Sylow 2-subgroups, 10 Sylow 3-subgroups, and 6 Sylow 5-subgroups. This implies that G must contain at least 48 distinct elements. But G has order 30. Therefore G is not simple.

Exercise 51   Suppose G is a group of order 56. Show that G cannot be a simple group.

Theorem 50   Suppose G is a group, P a Sylow p-subgroup of G, and $N_G(P)$ the normalizer of P in G. If H is a subgroup of G such that $N_G(P) \subseteq H \subseteq G$, then $H = N_G(H)$.

Proof: Let x be an element of G such that $x^{-1}Hx = H$. We must show that x belongs to H. Now $x^{-1}Px$ is a Sylow p-subgroup of H, say P'. Thus, there exists an element h in H such that $h^{-1}P'h = P$ (Theorem 47). It follows that $h^{-1}x^{-1}Pxh = P$, and so xh is an element of $N_G(P)$. Since $N_G(P) \subseteq H$, and h is in H, we have x is in H.

Theorem 51   Let G be a finite group and P a p-subgroup of G. If P is not a Sylow p-subgroup then $N_G(P)$ properly contains P.

Proof: This is immediate from Theorem 42, since if P has order p^s, then P must be normal in some subgroup P' of order p^{s+1}.

Exercise 52   Suppose P is a normal p-subgroup of a group G. Show that P is contained in every Sylow p-subgroup of G. (See Example 36.)

3-4. NILPOTENT GROUPS

In Sec. 2-3 the concepts of normal series and composition series of a group were discussed. In this section of Chapter 3 we introduce the concept of a central series for a group, and from this shall give a brief discussion of nilpotent groups.

Definition 36 Let G be a group. A series $\{e\} = H_0 \subseteq H_1 \subseteq H_2 \subseteq \cdots \subseteq H_s = G$, where $H_i/H_{i-1} \subseteq Z(G/H_{i-1})$ for $i = 1, 2, \ldots, s$, is called a *central series*. The series $\{e\} = H_0 \subseteq H_1 \subseteq H_2 \subseteq \cdots \subseteq H_i \subseteq H_{i+1} \subseteq \cdots$, where $H_{i+1}/H_i = Z(G/H_i)$, is called the *ascending central series* for G.

Example 38 The series $\{I\} \subset \{I, R'\} \subset \{I, R, R', R''\} \subset G$, where G is the group of symmetries of the square, is a central series for G. Since $Z(G) = \{I, R'\}$, we have $\{I, R'\}/\{I\} = Z(G/\{I\})$. Since $|G/\{I, R'\}| = 2^2$, $G/\{I, R'\}$ is Abelian. Thus $\{I, R, R', R''\}/\{I, R'\} \subseteq Z(G/\{I, R'\})$. Clearly, $G/\{I, R, R', R''\} = Z(G/\{I, R, R', R''\})$. It is to be noted that $\{I, R, R', R''\}/\{I, R'\} \neq Z(G/\{I, R'\})$, and therefore the series is not the ascending central series. However, the series $\{I\} \subset \{I, R'\} \subset G$ is the ascending central series for G.

Exercise 53 Find all central series for the group of symmetries of the square.

Definition 37 A group G is called *nilpotent* if it possesses a finite central series.

Since the group G of symmetries of the square possesses a finite central series, G is nilpotent. We shall shortly prove that this is true for all finite p-groups.

The reader may recall that it has been shown that a group G is solvable if, and only if, it possesses a finite normal series in which every factor is Abelian (Theorem 36). Since the factors of a central series are clearly Abelian, we see that every nilpotent group is also solvable.

Exercise 54 Give an example of a solvable group that is not nilpotent.

Remark 32 Clearly, if the ascending central series $\{e\} = H_0 \subseteq H_1 \subseteq H_2 \subseteq \cdots$ is such that $G = H_i$ for some i, then G is nilpotent. Suppose $\{e\} = H_0 \subseteq H_1 \subseteq H_2 \subseteq \cdots \subseteq H_c = G$ (where c is the least positive integer such that $H_c = G$). The number c is called the *class* of the nilpotent group G.

We may always form the series $\{e\} \subseteq Z(G) \subseteq G$. If G is non-Abelian, then, in order for this series to be a central series, we must have $\{e\} \subset Z(G)$ and $G/Z(G)$ Abelian. But $G/Z(G)$ cannot be cyclic (Remark 27). If $G/Z(G)$ is cyclic, then G is Abelian, and therefore nilpotent of class $c = 1$. If G is nilpotent of class $c = 1$, then G is Abelian.

Theorem 52 If G is a nilpotent p-group of class $c > 1$, then $[G : H_{c-1}]$ is divisible by p^2.

   Proof: Suppose $\{e\} \subset Z(G) \subset H_2 \subseteq \cdots \subseteq H_{c-1} \subseteq H_c = G$. Since $H_{c-1}/H_{c-2} = Z(G/H_{c-2})$, the result follows from Theorem 46.

Example 39 Consider the alternating group A_4 (see page 27). Since $Z(A_4) =$

$\{P_1\}$, there is no central series for A_4 (why?). Thus A_4 is not nilpotent. (Are any of the groups A_n nilpotent?)

Theorem 53 Every finite p-group G is nilpotent.

Proof: The ascending central series $\{e\} = H_0 \subseteq H_1 \subseteq H_2 \subseteq \ldots$, must terminate with $H_i = G$ for some i, since $Z(G) \neq \{e\}$ (Theorem 43). In fact, if $|G| = p^n$, then $H_n = G$. (Of course, G could be equal to H_i for some $i < n$, as is the case in Example 38.)

Exercise 55 Prove that a direct product of finite p-groups is nilpotent.

Remark 33 It is true that if H is a proper subgroup of the nilpotent group G, then H is also a proper subgroup of its normalizer $N_G(H)$. We do not prove this fact here, but shall use it to prove the following important theorem.

Theorem 54 Let G be a finite group. G is nilpotent if, and only if, G is the direct product of its Sylow subgroups.

Proof: Suppose G is nilpotent. Let P be a Sylow p-subgroup of G and $N_G(P)$ be the normalizer of P. Now the normalizer of $N_G(P)$ is $N_G(P)$, (Theorem 50). Thus, by the above remark, $N_G(P) = G$. Therefore P is a normal subgroup of G and we have that G is the direct product of its Sylow subgroups by Theorem 49.

Conversely, if G is the direct product of its Sylow subgroups, then G is nilpotent (Exercise 55).

It is immediate from Remark 33 that if H is a maximal subgroup of the nilpotent group G, then H must be normal. Now G/H contains no proper subgroups (since H is maximal) and thus is cyclic of prime order (Theorem 10). We also note that H contains the derived group of G (why?).

Theorem 55 If every maximal subgroup of a finite group G is normal, then G must be nilpotent.

Proof: $N_G(P)$ is its own normalizer by Theorem 50, where P is a Sylow p-subgroup of G. Now $N_G(P)$ is maximal, since otherwise we would have $N_G(P) \subset H \subset G$ where H is maximal. That this is not possible follows from Theorem 50 (H is normal by hypothesis and $N_G(P)$ cannot be contained in a proper normal subgroup of G). It follows that $N_G(P) = G$, and thus P is normal in G. Hence G is the direct product of its Sylow subgroups and is therefore nilpotent.

Exercise 56 Suppose G is a group and consider $I(G)$, the group of inner automorphisms of G (see Theorem 26). If $I(G) = \{e\}$, prove that G is nilpotent. Also, consider $I(I(G))$, the group of inner automorphisms of $I(G)$. If $I(I(G)) = \{e\}$, show that G is nilpotent.

3-5. THE FRATTINI SUBGROUP

Before leaving this chapter we consider the group G of symmetries of the regular octagon. Here $G = \{R_1, R_2, R_3, \ldots, R_{16}\}$ where $R_1, R_2, \ldots, R_8$ are rotations of $45°$, $90°, \ldots, 360°$ clockwise about the center 0 of the octagon, and $R_9, R_{10}, \ldots, R_{16}$ are reflections in the axes and diagonals as indicated in Fig. 2.

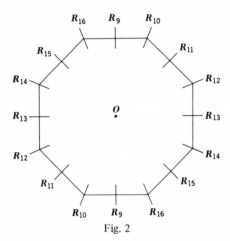

Fig. 2

The maximal subgroups of G are $\{R_1, R_2, R_3, R_4, R_5, R_6, R_7, R_8\}, \{R_2, R_4, R_6, R_8, R_9, R_{11}, R_{13}, R_{15}\}$, and $\{R_2, R_4, R_6, R_8, R_{10}, R_{12}, R_{14}, R_{16}\}$, and the intersection of these subgroups is the subgroup $\{R_2, R_4, R_6, R_8\}$.

Now if G is any group, the intersection of its maximal subgroups is a subgroup of G. It is called the *Frattini subgroup* of G and will be denoted by $F(G)$. Thus, for our group G above, we have $F(G) = \{R_2, R_4, R_6, R_8\}$. We note that $F(G)$ is nilpotent since it is a p-group (Theorem 53).

In general, if G is any finite group, then its Frattini subgroup is nilpotent. It is also true that if $F(G)$ contains the derived group G' of a finite group G then G will be nilpotent, as we shall prove in our next theorem. Note that in the group of the octagon (which is nilpotent since it is a p-group) we have $G' \subseteq F(G)$. In fact, in this example we have $G' = F(G)$ since the derived group of the group of symmetries of the octagon is also $\{R_2, R_4, R_6, R_8\}$, as the reader should show.

Exercise 57 In the group of the octagon, the maximal subgroups are normal (why?) and thus so is the intersection of the maximal subgroups (Exercise 15). Prove or disprove: The Frattini subgroup of a group is a normal subgroup.

Exercise 58   In a non-Abelian p-group G of order p^3 we have $Z(G) = G'$ (Remark 29).   Show that this is not necessarily true for a non-Abelian p-group of order p^4 by finding the center of the group of the octagon.

Theorem 56   If the Frattini subgroup of a finite group G contains the derived group of G, then G is nilpotent.

Proof: Suppose P is a Sylow p-subgroup of G. Now $N_G(P) = G$. For suppose otherwise.   Then $N_G(P) \subseteq H$ where H is a maximal subgroup of G. Since $F(G) \subseteq H$ (Why?) and $G' \subseteq F(G)$, $G' \subseteq H$.   But since G/G' is Abelian, we have $H \triangle G$ (Theorem 29).   That this is not possible follows from Theorem 50.   Hence $N_G(P) = G$. G is then the direct product of its Sylow subgroups (Theorem 49) and therefore nilpotent (Theorem 54).

Thus we know that if $F(G)$ contains G' then G is nilpotent.   But when does $F(G)$ contain G'?

Theorem 57   The Frattini subgroup of a group G contains G' if, and only if, all maximal subgroups of G are normal.

Proof: Let $H_1, H_2, \ldots$ be the maximal subgroups of G and suppose each is normal.   Now the quotient groups G/H_i are Abelian since $|G/H_i|$ is a prime (Theorem 10).   Thus $G' \subseteq H_i$ for each i (Exercise 27), and so $G' \subseteq F(G)$.

Conversely, suppose $G' \subseteq F(G)$.   If H is a maximal subgroup of G, then $G' \subseteq H$ (since $F(G) \subseteq H$).   Thus H is normal in G (Theorem 29).

Theorem 58   The Frattini subgroup of a nilpotent group G contains G'.

Proof: This is immediate since the maximal subgroups of G are normal (see comment following Theorem 54).

Exercise 59   In the group G of symmetries of the octagon, note that the quotient group $G/F(G)$ is solvable and cyclic (why?).   Prove that if G is any finite group then G is solvable if, and only if, $G/F(G)$ is solvable and that G is cyclic if, and only if, $G/F(G)$ is cyclic.

4

Groups of Special Order

4-1. GROUPS OF ORDER 4 AND 6

In this chapter we shall apply results found earlier to groups of specific orders, and develop some additional theory. It is realized that much of this material could well have been presented in previous sections, but it is preferred to discuss it now.

We have seen that there are two groups of order p^2 (Exercise 49), and that both must be Abelian (Remark 28). One of them is cyclic generated by, say a, and in the noncyclic group all elements other than the identity must have order p. Tables 10 and 11 are the group tables for the two groups of order 4. The second of these is called the *Klein four-group*.

TABLE 10

	e	a	a^2	a^3
e	e	a	a^2	a^3
a	a	a^2	a^3	e
a^2	a^2	a^3	e	a
a^3	a^3	e	a	a^2

TABLE 11

	e	a	b	ab
e	e	a	b	ab
a	a	e	ab	b
b	b	ab	e	a
ab	ab	b	a	e

Exercise 60   Show that the Klein four-group is a direct product of two cyclic groups, each having order two (see Sec. 2-4).

There is at least one group of order 6; the cyclic group of that order. Since there can be only one Abelian group of order 6 (Remark 31), any other group of order 6 would have to be non-Abelian. Question: Do non-Abelian groups of order 6 exist, and if so, how many are there? (That is, how many nonisomorphic non-Abelian groups of order 6 are there?)

Now if such a group does exist, then all elements (other than e) cannot have order 2 (Exercise 1). Thus there exists an element, say x, of order 3. (The reader should, at this point, recall Exercise 8.) Let y be an element other than x, x^2, and $x^3 = e$, and consider the set $G = \{e,x,x^2,y,xy,x^2y\}$. One easily shows that the elements in G are distinct (do this!). The problem now is to see how Table 12 should be filled in so that G will be a non-Abelian group of order 6.

TABLE 12

	e	x	x^2	y	xy	x^2y
e						
x						
x^2						
y						
xy						
x^2y						

Since closure must hold, y^2 must be an element in G. Clearly y^2 cannot be equal to xy or x^2y. Thus it must be the case that $y^2 = e$, $y^2 = x$, or $y^2 = x^2$. $y^2 = x$ or $y^2 = x^2$ each implies that y is an element of order 3. That is, $y^3 = e$. But then we would have $xy = e$ or $x^2y = e$. Since neither of these is possible, we conclude that $y^2 = e$.

Now yx must also belong to G. In fact, it must be the case that $yx = x^2y$ (why?). This implies that $(xy)^2 = e$. Thus we have that $x^3 = y^2 = (xy)^2 = e$, and the "multiplication" table for G must be as shown.

TABLE 13

	e	x	x^2	y	xy	x^2y
e	e	x	x^2	y	xy	x^2y
x	x	x^2	e	xy	x^2y	y
x^2	x^2	e	x	x^2y	y	xy
y	y	x^2y	xy	e	x^2	x
xy	xy	y	x^2y	x	e	x^2
x^2y	x^2y	xy	y	x^2	x	e

It is to be pointed out that the associative property was used to form some of the above products. Of course, the associative property must hold in all cases in order for G to be a group. It does. Therefore G is a non-Abelian group of order 6. It is clear that any other non-Abelian group of order 6 must be isomorphic to G.

Exercise 61   Show that S_3 (see Example 4) is isomorphic to the group G above.

4-2. GROUPS OF ORDER pq AND p^2q

A group of order 6 is a specific example of a group of order pq where p and q are distinct primes. We shall now briefly discuss groups of this type.

We know that there is only one Abelian group G of order pq; the cyclic group of this order. Question: Is there a non-Abelian group of order pq? The answer is no if p is not a factor of $q - 1$; as we now see.

Theorem 59   Let G be a group of order pq where p and q are primes with $p < q$. If p does not divide $q - 1$, then G is cyclic.

Proof: The number of Sylow p-subgroups of G is $1 + kp$ (Theorem 48). Since this number is a divisor of pq, and p is not a divisor of $q - 1$, it follows that G contains only one Sylow p-subgroup, say P. Since the number of Sylow q-subgroups of G is a divisor of pq of the form $1 + kq$, and q does not divide $p - 1$ ($p < q$), G contains only one Sylow q-subgroup, say Q. Now P and Q are normal in G (Remark 30). Thus $G = P \times Q$ (Theorem 49). That G is cyclic follows from Exercise 42.

Note: Theorem 59 does not apply to groups of order 6. In fact, it does not apply to any group of order pq where $p = 2$. Yet for groups of order say, 15, 33, 51, 35, 65, or 77, it does, implying the existence of just one group for each of these orders.

One should now wonder what the answer to our question is if p *does* divide $q - 1$. Here, if G is to be non-Abelian, G must contain q Sylow p-subgroups (since otherwise it will have only one, implying that G is cyclic as in Theorem 59). That such a group does indeed exist is not shown here. But we do observe the following:

G has only one Sylow q-subgroup, say Q, and q Sylow p-subgroups. Let P be a Sylow p-subgroup. Suppose Q is generated by x and P is generated by y. Then $x^q = e$, $y^p = e$. Now P is not normal (Remark 30), but Q is. Thus $y^{-1}xy$ is in Q, and so $y^{-1}xy = x^i$ for some i. One can show that i^p must be congruent to 1 mod q while i is not congruent to 1 mod q. That is, we have $i^p \equiv 1 \pmod{q}$

and $i \not\equiv 1 \pmod{q}$. The relations $x^q = e$, $y^p = e$, $y^{-1}xy = x^i$ where $i^p \equiv 1 \pmod{q}$ and $i \not\equiv 1 \pmod{q}$ define our non-Abelian group G of order pq where p divides $q - 1$.

We return briefly to the case $p = 2$ and $q = 3$. Suppose a is an element of order 3 and b is an element of order 2. Then $a^3 = e$, $b^2 = e$. We want $b^{-1}ab = a^i$ where $i^2 \equiv 1 \pmod{3}$ and $i \not\equiv 1 \pmod{3}$. It follows that 3 must divide $i + 1$, and so $i = 2, 5, 8, \ldots$. Thus $b^{-1}ab = a^2$. This relation leads us to Table 14. (Compare with Table 13.)

TABLE 14

	e	a	a^2	b	ab	a^2b
e	e	a	a^2	b	ab	a^2b
a	a	a^2	e	ab	a^2b	b
a^2	a^2	e	a	a^2b	b	ab
b	b	a^2b	ab	e	a^2	a
ab	ab	b	a^2b	a	e	a^2
a^2b	a^2b	ab	b	a^2	a	e

Exercise 62 Construct the non-Abelian group of order 10.

Theorem 60 Let G be a group of order p^2q where p and q are primes, $p < q$, and p does not divide $q - 1$. Then G is Abelian.

Proof: The number of Sylow p-subgroups of G is $1 + kp$ and divides p^2q. Since $1 + kp$ and p are relatively prime it follows that $1 + kp = 1$, or $1 + kp = q$. But p does not divide $q - 1$, implying that G contains only one Sylow p-subgroup, say P. The number of Sylow q-subgroups is $1 + kq$. Since $1 + kq$ and q are relatively prime and $1 + kq$ is a divisor of p^2q, we have $1 + kq = 1, p$, or p^2. Now $1 + kq = p^2$ implies $kq = p^2 - 1$, which implies that q divides $p - 1$ (which cannot be since $p < q$) or q divides $p + 1$ (which also cannot be, since then we must have $q = 3$ and $p = 2$). Therefore G contains only one Sylow q-subgroup, say Q. Thus $G = P \times Q$, and since P and Q are Abelian, so is G.

Exercise 63 In Theorem 60, suppose $q < p$ and q is not a divisor of $p^2 - 1$. Prove G is Abelian.

Note: Groups of the type described in Theorems 59 and 60, and in Exercise 63 are not simple groups. Clearly, they are solvable (Example 29).

As a closing remark in this section we note that the results obtained above for groups of order p^2q do not apply to groups of order 12. There do exist 5 distinct groups of order 12, and the reader is asked to describe these in the following exercise. (Recall that we have discussed one of these in some detail previously; namely, A_4.)

Exercise 64 Show the existence of 5 nonisomorphic groups of order 12. (*Hint*: If G is a group of order 12 that is not isomorphic to A_4, then G contains an element of order 6.)

4-3. GROUPS OF ORDER p^3

We now discuss groups of order p^3, p a prime.

It is clear that there exists 3 nonisomorphic Abelian groups of order p^3. For suppose H is cyclic of order p^2 generated by a and K is cyclic of order p generated by b. Then $G = H \times K$ is Abelian of order p^3. If H is cyclic of order p generated by a, K is cyclic of order p generated by b, and M is cyclic of order p generated by c, then $G = H \times K \times M$ is Abelian of order p^3. The third Abelian group of order p^3 is the cyclic group of that order.

For the special case $p = 2$, we have 3 Abelian groups of order 8. Tables 15 and 16 are the multiplication tables for two of these groups.

We now determine the non-Abelian groups of order 8. Such a group cannot

TABLE 15

	e	a	a^2	a^3	b	ab	a^2b	a^3b
e	e	a	a^2	a^3	b	ab	a^2b	a^3b
a	a	a^2	a^3	e	ab	a^2b	a^3b	b
a^2	a^2	a^3	e	a	a^2b	a^3b	b	ab
a^3	a^3	e	a	a^2	a^3b	b	ab	a^2b
b	b	ab	a^2b	a^3b	e	a	a^2	a^3
ab	ab	a^2b	a^3b	b	a	a^2	a^3	e
a^2b	a^2b	a^3b	b	ab	a^2	a^3	e	a
a^3b	a^3b	b	ab	a^2b	a^3	e	a	a^2

TABLE 16

	e	a	b	c	ab	ac	bc	abc
e	e	a	b	c	ab	ac	bc	abc
a	a	e	ab	ac	b	c	abc	bc
b	b	ab	e	bc	a	abc	c	ac
c	c	ac	bc	e	abc	a	b	ab
ab	ab	b	a	abc	e	bc	ac	c
ac	ac	c	abc	a	bc	e	ab	b
bc	bc	abc	c	b	ac	ab	e	a
abc	abc	bc	ac	ab	c	b	a	e

have an element of order 8, and all elements other than e cannot be of order 2 (why?). Thus there must be an element of order 4, say x. Suppose y is an element other than e, x, x^2, or x^3, and consider the set $G = \{e,x,x^2,x^3,y,xy,x^2y, x^3y\}$. Clearly, $y^2 \neq y, xy, x^2y$ or x^3y. If $y^2 = x$ then y would be an element of order 8. Likewise if $y^2 = x^3$. Thus we have the two possibilities: (i) $y^2 = e$ or (ii) $y^2 = x^2$.

(i) Suppose $y^2 = e$. Now yx must be equal to x^2y or x^3y. (Show that if $yx = xy$, we get the group of Table 15.) For $yx = x^2y$ we obtain $x = y^{-1}x^2y$, which implies that $x^2 = e$. Therefore, it must be the case that $yx = x^3y$ (or that $(xy)^2 = e$). The relations $x^4 = e$, $y^2 = e$, and $(xy)^2 = e$ define a non-Abelian group of order 8. Table 17 is its multiplication table.

TABLE 17

	e	x	x^2	x^3	y	xy	x^2y	x^3y
e	e	x	x^2	x^3	y	xy	x^2y	x^3y
x	x	x^2	x^3	e	xy	x^2y	x^3y	y
x^2	x^2	x^3	e	x	x^2y	x^3y	y	xy
x^3	x^3	e	x	x^2	x^3y	y	xy	x^2y
y	y	x^3y	x^2y	xy	e	x^3	x^2	x
xy	xy	y	x^3y	x^2y	x	e	x^3	x^2
x^2y	x^2y	xy	y	x^3y	x^2	x	e	x^3
x^3y	x^3y	x^2y	xy	y	x^3	x^2	x	e

Exercise 65 Show that the group of symmetries of the square (Example 3) is isomorphic to the above group.

(ii) Suppose $y^2 = x^2$. Now yx must be x^2y or x^3y. (If $yx = xy$, we again obtain the group of Table 15.) For $yx = x^2y$ (where $x^2 = y^2$) we have $yx = y^3$, which implies that $x = y^2 = x^2$. Therefore it must be the case that $yx = x^3y$ (or $(xy)^2 = e$). The relations $x^4 = e$, $x^2 = y^2$, and $(xy)^2 = e$ define a second non-Abelian group of order 8. This group is called the *quaternion group* and Table 18 is its multiplication table.

So far, we have seen that there are three Abelian groups of order p^3 where p is any prime, and two non-Abelian groups when $p = 2$. It remains to see how many non-Abelian groups G exist of order p^3 where $p \neq 2$. As in the case $p = 2$, there are also two. We discuss one of these here.

In either of the groups, if G is to be non-Abelian it does not contain an element of order p^3. Suppose all elements other than e have order p. Now $Z(G)$ has order p (Theorem 46). The quotient group $G/Z(G)$, having order p^2, must be defined by the relations $a^p = e$, $b^p = e$, $ab = ba$. ($G/Z(G)$ is not cyclic by

TABLE 18

	e	x	x^2	x^3	y	xy	x^2y	x^3y
e	e	x	x^2	x^3	y	xy	x^2y	x^3y
x	x	x^2	x^3	e	xy	x^2y	x^3y	y
x^2	x^2	x^3	e	x	x^2y	x^3y	y	xy
x^3	x^3	e	x	x^2	x^3y	y	xy	x^2y
y	y	x^3y	x^2y	xy	x^2	x	e	x^3
xy	xy	y	x^3y	x^2y	x^3	x^2	x	e
x^2y	x^2y	xy	y	x^3y	e	x^3	x^2	x
x^3y	x^3y	x^2y	xy	y	x	e	x^3	x^2

Remark 27. Also see Exercise 49.) If we consider the "natural homomorphism" (see note following Theorem 21) $\varphi : G \to G/Z(G)$, where $\varphi(x) = a$ and $\varphi(y) = b$, then we have that $\varphi(x^{-1}y^{-1}xy) = a^{-1}b^{-1}ab = e$. This implies that $x^{-1}y^{-1}xy$ is in the kernel of φ, which is $Z(G)$. Now $x^{-1}y^{-1}xy \neq e$, since otherwise G would be an Abelian group (why?) Therefore $x^{-1}y^{-1}xy$ is an element of order p and generates $Z(G)$. If we set $x^{-1}y^{-1}xy = z$, then we have that $xy = yxz$, $xz = zx$, and $yz = zy$. The relations $x^p = e$, $y^p = e$, $z^p = e$, $xy = yxz$, $xz = zx$, and $yz = zy$ define our non-Abelian group of order p^3, $p \neq 2$.

Exercise 66   Construct a non-Abelian group of order 27.

Returning briefly to the quaternion group G defined by Table 18, we note that the following are the subgroups of this group: $\{e\}$, $H = \{e,x^2\}$, $K_1 = \{e,x,x^2,x^3\}$, $K_2 = \{e,x^2,y,x^2y\}$, $K_3 = \{e,xy,x^2,x^3y\}$, and G. Now K_1, K_2, and K_3 are normal in G since $[G:K_i] = 2$. H is normal in G since $H = Z(G)$. Thus we have our first example of a non-Abelian group with the property that all of its subgroups are normal. Such a group is called a *Hamiltonian group*.

We remark that by a generalized quaternion group is meant a group of order $2^n (n > 2)$ generated by elements x and y such that $x^{2^{n-1}} = e$, $yxy^{-1} = x^{-1}$, and $x^{2^{n-2}} = y^2$.

Exercise 67   Find an example of a Hamiltonian group other than the quaternion group.

4-4.   GROUPS OF ORDER 16

Thus far we have seen the existence of but one group of order 2, two groups of order 4, and five groups of order 8. In this section we discuss the fourteen

TABLE 19

	(e,e)	(e,a)	(e,b)	(e,ab)	(x,e)	(x,a)	(x,b)	(x,ab)	(x^2,e)	(x^2,a)	(x^2,b)	(x^2,ab)	(x^3,e)	(x^3,a)	(x^3,b)	(x^3,ab)
(e,e)	(e,e)	(e,a)	(e,b)	(e,ab)	(x,e)	(x,a)	(x,b)	(x,ab)	(x^2,e)	(x^2,a)	(x^2,b)	(x^2,ab)	(x^3,e)	(x^3,a)	(x^3,b)	(x^3,ab)
(e,a)	(e,a)	(e,e)	(e,ab)	(e,b)	(x,a)	(x,e)	(x,ab)	(x,b)	(x^2,a)	(x^2,e)	(x^2,ab)	(x^2,b)	(x^3,a)	(x^3,e)	(x^3,ab)	(x^3,b)
(e,b)	(e,b)	(e,ab)	(e,e)	(e,a)	(x,b)	(x,ab)	(x,e)	(x,a)	(x^2,b)	(x^2,ab)	(x^2,e)	(x^2,a)	(x^3,b)	(x^3,ab)	(x^3,e)	(x^3,a)
(e,ab)	(e,ab)	(e,b)	(e,a)	(e,e)	(x,ab)	(x,b)	(x,a)	(x,e)	(x^2,ab)	(x^2,b)	(x^2,a)	(x^2,e)	(x^3,ab)	(x^3,b)	(x^3,a)	(x^3,e)
(x,e)	(x,e)	(x,a)	(x,b)	(x,ab)	(x^2,e)	(x^2,a)	(x^2,b)	(x^2,ab)	(x^3,e)	(x^3,a)	(x^3,b)	(x^3,ab)	(e,e)	(e,a)	(e,b)	(e,ab)
(x,a)	(x,a)	(x,e)	(x,ab)	(x,b)	(x^2,a)	(x^2,e)	(x^2,ab)	(x^2,b)	(x^3,a)	(x^3,e)	(x^3,ab)	(x^3,b)	(e,a)	(e,e)	(e,ab)	(e,b)
(x,b)	(x,b)	(x,ab)	(x,e)	(x,a)	(x^2,b)	(x^2,ab)	(x^2,e)	(x^2,a)	(x^3,b)	(x^3,ab)	(x^3,e)	(x^3,a)	(e,b)	(e,ab)	(e,e)	(e,a)
(x,ab)	(x,ab)	(x,b)	(x,a)	(x,e)	(x^2,ab)	(x^2,b)	(x^2,a)	(x^2,e)	(x^3,ab)	(x^3,b)	(x^3,a)	(x^3,e)	(e,ab)	(e,b)	(e,a)	(e,e)
(x^2,e)	(x^2,e)	(x^2,a)	(x^2,b)	(x^2,ab)	(x^3,e)	(x^3,a)	(x^3,b)	(x^3,ab)	(e,e)	(e,a)	(e,b)	(e,ab)	(x,e)	(x,a)	(x,b)	(x,ab)
(x^2,a)	(x^2,a)	(x^2,e)	(x^2,ab)	(x^2,b)	(x^3,a)	(x^3,e)	(x^3,ab)	(x^3,b)	(e,a)	(e,e)	(e,ab)	(e,b)	(x,a)	(x,e)	(x,ab)	(x,b)
(x^2,b)	(x^2,b)	(x^2,ab)	(x^2,e)	(x^2,a)	(x^3,b)	(x^3,ab)	(x^3,e)	(x^3,a)	(e,b)	(e,ab)	(e,e)	(e,a)	(x,b)	(x,ab)	(x,e)	(x,a)
(x^2,ab)	(x^2,ab)	(x^2,b)	(x^2,a)	(x^2,e)	(x^3,ab)	(x^3,b)	(x^3,a)	(x^3,e)	(e,ab)	(e,b)	(e,a)	(e,e)	(x,ab)	(x,b)	(x,a)	(x,e)
(x^3,e)	(x^3,e)	(x^3,a)	(x^3,b)	(x^3,ab)	(e,e)	(e,a)	(e,b)	(e,ab)	(x,e)	(x,a)	(x,b)	(x,ab)	(x^2,e)	(x^2,a)	(x^2,b)	(x^2,ab)
(x^3,a)	(x^3,a)	(x^3,e)	(x^3,ab)	(x^3,b)	(e,a)	(e,e)	(e,ab)	(e,b)	(x,a)	(x,e)	(x,ab)	(x,b)	(x^2,a)	(x^2,e)	(x^2,ab)	(x^2,b)
(x^3,b)	(x^3,b)	(x^3,ab)	(x^3,e)	(x^3,a)	(e,b)	(e,ab)	(e,e)	(e,a)	(x,b)	(x,ab)	(x,e)	(x,a)	(x^2,b)	(x^2,ab)	(x^2,e)	(x^2,a)
(x^3,ab)	(x^3,ab)	(x^3,b)	(x^3,a)	(x^3,e)	(e,ab)	(e,b)	(e,a)	(e,e)	(x,ab)	(x,b)	(x,a)	(x,e)	(x^2,ab)	(x^2,b)	(x^2,a)	(x^2,e)

groups of order 16. (There are 51 groups of order 32, and 267 groups of order 64.)

Abelian Groups of Order 16

Let H_1 be the cyclic group of order 2, H_2 the cyclic group of order 4, H_3 the noncyclic group of order 4 (Table 11), and H_4 the cyclic group of order 8. There are four distinct Abelian groups of order 16 besides the cyclic group of that order. These may be described as follows: $G_1 = H_1 \times H_1 \times H_1 \times H_1, G_2 = H_2 \times H_2, G_3 = H_2 \times H_3, G_4 = H_1 \times H_4$. Table 19 is the group table for G_3.

Exercise 68 If H_5 and H_6 are the groups of Tables 17 and 18 respectively, and $G_5 = H_1 \times H_5$, $G_6 = H_1 \times H_6$, then G_5 and G_6 are Abelian groups of order 16. Show that G_5 is isomorphic to one of the groups G_i above, as is G_6.

Non-Abelian Groups of Order 16

In describing these groups we distinguish two cases: (i) the center has order 2, and (ii) the center has order 4. The center cannot have order 8 by Theorem 45. (See also Remark 27.)

(i) In the group G of symmetries of the regular octagon (Sec. 3-5) we note that $R_4{}^2 = R_8$, $R_2{}^2 = R_4$, $R_3{}^2 = R_2{}^{-1}$, $R_9{}^2 = R_8$, $R_4 = R_2{}^{-1}R_9{}^{-1}R_2R_9$, and $R_2 = R_3{}^{-1}R_9{}^{-1}R_3R_9$. These relations completely determine the group of the octagon. (The reader should show this.) More generally, the relations $a^2 = e$, $b^2 = a$, $c^2 = b^{-1}$, $d^2 = e$, $a = b^{-1}d^{-1}bd$, $b = c^{-1}d^{-1}cd$, determine a non-Abelian group of order 16. Its group table is given in Table 20.

The relations $a^2 = e$, $b^2 = a$, $c^2 = b^{-1}$, $d^2 = a$, $a = b^{-1}d^{-1}bd$, and $b = c^{-1}d^{-1}cd$ also define a non-Abelian group of order 16 (whose center has order 2), as do the relations $a^2 = e$, $b^2 = a$, $c^2 = b$, $d^2 = e$, $a = b^{-1}d^{-1}bd$, and $b = c^{-1}d^{-1}cd$. There are three non-Abelian groups of order 16 whose centers have order 2.

(ii) We now discuss the non-Abelian groups of order 16 that have a center of order 4. Here we again distinguish two cases: (1) the center is cyclic (Table 10) and (2) the center is noncyclic (Table 11).

1. There are two non-Abelian groups of order 16 having a center which is the cyclic group of order 4. These may be described as follows: Let x be a generator for the center. The relations $a^2 = b^2 = c^2 = e$, $x^2 = a$, and $a = b^{-1}c^{-1}bc$ (or $(bc)^2 = a$) determine one of the groups; $a^2 = b^2 = e$, $c^2 = x$, $x^2 = a$, and $a = b^{-1}c^{-1}bc$ determine the other. Table 21 is the group table for the first of these groups.

2. There are four non-Abelian groups of order 16 having a center which is noncyclic of order 4. The relations $a^2 = e$, $b^2 = y$, $x = a^{-1}b^{-1}ab$, and the relations

TABLE 20

	a	b	c	d	ab	ac	ad	bc	bd	cd	abc	abd	acd	bcd	abcd	e
a	e	ab	ac	ad	b	c	d	abc	abd	acd	bc	bd	cd	abcd	bcd	a
b	ab	e	bc	bd	a	abc	abd	c	d	bcd	ac	ad	abcd	cd	acd	b
c	ac	bc	e	cd	abc	a	acd	b	bcd	d	ab	abcd	ad	bd	abd	c
d	ad	bd	cd	e	abd	acd	a	bcd	b	c	abcd	ab	ac	bc	abc	d
ab	b	a	abc	abd	e	bc	bd	ac	ad	abcd	c	d	bcd	acd	cd	ab
ac	c	abc	a	acd	bc	e	cd	ab	abcd	ad	b	bcd	d	abd	bd	ac
ad	d	abd	acd	a	bd	cd	e	abcd	ab	ac	bcd	b	c	abc	bc	ad
bc	abc	c	b	bcd	ac	ab	abcd	e	cd	bd	a	acd	abd	d	ad	bc
bd	abd	d	bcd	b	ad	abcd	ab	cd	e	bc	acd	a	abc	c	ac	bd
cd	acd	bcd	d	c	abcd	ad	ac	bd	bc	e	abd	abc	a	b	ab	cd
abc	bc	ac	ab	abcd	c	b	bcd	a	acd	abd	e	cd	bd	ad	d	abc
abd	bd	ad	abcd	ab	d	bcd	b	acd	a	abc	cd	e	bc	ac	c	abd
acd	cd	abcd	ad	ac	bcd	d	c	abd	abc	a	bd	bc	e	ab	b	acd
bcd	abcd	cd	bd	bc	acd	abd	abc	d	c	b	ad	ac	ab	e	a	bcd
abcd	bcd	acd	abd	abc	cd	bd	bc	ad	ac	ab	d	c	b	a	e	abcd
e	a	b	c	d	ab	ac	ad	bc	bd	cd	abc	abd	acd	bcd	abcd	e

TABLE 21

	e	*a*	*b*	*c*	*x*	*ab*	*ac*	*ax*	*bc*	*bx*	*cx*	*abc*	*abx*	*acx*	*bcx*	*abcx*
e	*e*	*a*	*b*	*c*	*x*	*ab*	*ac*	*ax*	*bc*	*bx*	*cx*	*abc*	*abx*	*acx*	*bcx*	*abcx*
a	*a*	*e*	*ab*	*ac*	*ax*	*b*	*c*	*x*	*abc*	*abx*	*acx*	*bc*	*bx*	*cx*	*abcx*	*bcx*
b	*b*	*ab*	*e*	*bc*	*bx*	*a*	*abc*	*abx*	*c*	*x*	*bcx*	*ac*	*ax*	*abcx*	*cx*	*acx*
c	*c*	*ac*	*bc*	*e*	*cx*	*abc*	*a*	*acx*	*b*	*bcx*	*x*	*ab*	*abcx*	*ax*	*bx*	*abx*
x	*x*	*ax*	*bx*	*cx*	*e*	*abx*	*acx*	*a*	*bcx*	*b*	*c*	*abcx*	*ab*	*ac*	*bc*	*abc*
ab	*ab*	*b*	*a*	*abc*	*abx*	*e*	*bc*	*bx*	*ac*	*ax*	*abcx*	*c*	*x*	*bcx*	*acx*	*cx*
ac	*ac*	*c*	*abc*	*a*	*acx*	*bc*	*e*	*cx*	*ab*	*abcx*	*ax*	*b*	*bcx*	*x*	*abx*	*bx*
ax	*ax*	*x*	*abx*	*acx*	*a*	*bx*	*cx*	*e*	*abcx*	*ab*	*ac*	*bcx*	*b*	*c*	*abc*	*bc*
bc	*bc*	*abc*	*c*	*b*	*bcx*	*ac*	*ab*	*abcx*	*e*	*cx*	*bx*	*a*	*acx*	*abx*	*x*	*ax*
bx	*bx*	*abx*	*x*	*bcx*	*b*	*ax*	*abcx*	*ab*	*cx*	*e*	*bc*	*acx*	*a*	*abc*	*c*	*ac*
cx	*cx*	*acx*	*bcx*	*x*	*c*	*abcx*	*ax*	*ac*	*bx*	*bc*	*e*	*abx*	*abc*	*a*	*b*	*ab*
abc	*abc*	*bc*	*ac*	*ab*	*abcx*	*c*	*b*	*bcx*	*a*	*acx*	*abx*	*e*	*cx*	*bx*	*ax*	*x*
abx	*abx*	*bx*	*ax*	*abcx*	*ab*	*x*	*bcx*	*b*	*acx*	*a*	*abc*	*cx*	*e*	*bc*	*ac*	*c*
acx	*acx*	*cx*	*abcx*	*ax*	*ac*	*bcx*	*x*	*c*	*abx*	*abc*	*a*	*bx*	*bc*	*e*	*ab*	*b*
bcx	*bcx*	*abcx*	*cx*	*bx*	*bc*	*acx*	*abx*	*abc*	*x*	*c*	*b*	*ax*	*ac*	*ab*	*e*	*a*
abcx	*abcx*	*bcx*	*acx*	*abx*	*abc*	*cx*	*bx*	*bc*	*ax*	*ac*	*ab*	*x*	*c*	*b*	*a*	*e*

TABLE 22

	e	a	b	x	y	ab	ax	ay	bx	by	xy	abx	aby	axy	bxy	abxy
e	e	a	b	x	y	ab	ax	ay	bx	by	xy	abx	aby	axy	bxy	abxy
a	a	x	ab	ax	ay	bx	e	xy	abx	aby	axy	b	bxy	y	abxy	by
b	b	abx	x	bx	by	a	ab	abxy	e	xy	bxy	ax	ay	aby	y	axy
x	x	ax	bx	e	xy	abx	a	axy	b	bxy	y	ab	abxy	ay	by	aby
y	y	ay	by	xy	e	aby	axy	a	bxy	b	x	abxy	ab	ax	bx	abx
ab	ab	b	ax	abx	aby	x	bx	by	a	axy	abxy	e	xy	bxy	ay	y
ax	ax	e	abx	a	axy	b	x	y	ab	abxy	ay	bx	by	xy	aby	bxy
ay	ay	xy	aby	axy	a	bxy	y	x	abxy	ab	ax	by	bx	e	abx	b
bx	bx	ab	e	b	bxy	ax	abx	aby	x	y	by	a	axy	abxy	xy	ay
by	by	abxy	xy	bxy	b	ay	aby	abx	y	x	bx	axy	a	ab	e	ax
xy	xy	axy	bxy	y	x	abxy	ay	ax	by	bx	e	aby	abx	a	b	ab
abx	abx	bx	a	ab	abxy	e	b	bxy	ax	ay	aby	x	y	by	axy	xy
aby	aby	by	axy	abxy	ab	xy	bxy	b	ay	ax	abx	y	x	bx	a	e
axy	axy	y	abxy	ay	ax	by	xy	e	aby	abx	a	bxy	b	x	ab	bx
bxy	bxy	aby	y	by	bx	axy	abxy	ab	xy	e	b	ay	ax	abx	x	a
abxy	abxy	bxy	ay	aby	abx	y	by	bx	axy	a	ab	xy	e	b	ax	x

$a^2 = x$, $b^2 = y$, $x = a^{-1}b^{-1}ab$ determine two of these groups where x and y are generators for the center ($x^2 = y^2 = e$). The remaining two groups are determined by the relations $a^2 = x$, $b^2 = e$, $x = a^{-1}b^{-1}ab$, $x^2 = y^2 = e$, and the relations $a^2 = b^2 = x$, $x = a^{-1}b^{-1}ab$, $x^2 = y^2 = e$. Table 22 is the group table for the second of these groups.

Exercise 69 One of the groups defined by Tables 21 and 22 is Hamiltonian. Which one? (See Exercise 67.)

5

Galois Theory

5-1. DEFINITION OF A FIELD
EXTENSION FIELDS

In Chapter 2 we mentioned that the general nth degree equation is not solvable by radicals unless the symmetric group S_n is a solvable group (see Remark 23). It is our purpose here in this final chapter to discuss this fact in some detail. To do so will necessitate a discussion of a mathematical system known as a field.

Although entire books have been written on field theory, we confine our discussion here to a brief introduction, and mention only those facts needed to relate the concepts of a field, a group, and solutions to polynomial equations. Because we wish not to get too involved with field theory as such, several statements are made without proof. For the interested reader, these proofs may be found in most books dealing with the theory of fields.

Definition 38 Let K be a set containing at least two elements and suppose that there are two binary operations which are denoted by + and · defined on the elements of K. We call K a *field* with respect to + and · if

1. $a + b = b + a$ for all a and b in K.
2. $(a + b) + c = a + (b + c)$ for all a, b, and c in K.
3. K contains an element denoted by 0 such that $a + 0 = a$ for all a in K. (0 is called the zero element, or additive identity element of K.)
4. For each element a in K there is an element denoted by $-a$ in K such that $a + -a = 0$. ($-a$ is called the additive inverse of a.)
5. $ab = ba$ for all a and b in K.
6. $(ab)c = a(bc)$ for all a, b, and c in K.

7. K contains an element denoted by 1 such that $a \cdot 1 = a$ for all a in K. (1 is called the unity element, or multiplicative identity of K.)

8. For each element $a \neq 0$ in K, there is an element denoted by a^{-1} (or $\frac{1}{a}$) in K such that $a \cdot a^{-1} = 1$. (a^{-1} is called the multiplicative inverse of a.)

9. $a(b + c) = ab + ac$ for all a, b, and c in K. (Distributive property.)

Note: The elements of a field form a group with respect to +, and the elements $\neq 0$ form a group with respect to ·

Definition 39   A subset F of a field K is a *subfield* of K if F is itself a field relative to the binary operations defined in K.

Remark 34   To show that F is a subfield of the field K, we need only show that $a + b$, $a \cdot b$, and $-a$ are in F whenever a and b are in F, and that a^{-1} is in F whenever $a \neq 0$ is in F.

Exercise 70   Show that if F_1 and F_2 are subfields of the field F then $F_1 \cap F_2$ is also a subfield of F.

Definition 40   Let F and K be fields. If F is a subfield of K, we call K an *extension field* of F.

Example 40   The set C of complex numbers, the set R of real numbers, and the set Q of rational numbers are all examples of fields with respect to the usual operations of + and ·. C is an extension field of R and an extension field of Q. R is an extension of Q.

Example 41   Let $K = \{0,1,2,\dots, p-1\}$ where p is any prime and suppose + and · are defined on K as being ordinary addition and multiplication "reduced" modulo p. (See Example 11.) Then K is a field. (If a field consists of a finite number of elements it is called a *Galois field*.)

Example 42   Suppose Q is the field of rational numbers and let $Q(\sqrt{2}) = \{a + b\sqrt{2}\,;\, a$ and b are in $Q\}$. $Q(\sqrt{2})$ is a subfield of the field R of real numbers (the reader should show this) and is called the *subfield of R* obtained by adjoining $\sqrt{2}$ to the field Q.

Remark 35   Suppose K is an extension field of F and let a be an element of K. Let S be the collection of all subfields of K that contain F and a. The intersection of all elements of S shall be denoted by $F(a)$. Now $F(a)$ is a subfield of K (Exercise 70). It is the smallest subfield of K that contains both F and a, and we call it the *subfield* obtained by adjoining a to F.

Exercise 71   Show that $(Q(\sqrt{2}))(\sqrt{3})$ is a subfield of the field R of real numbers. Here, $(Q(\sqrt{2}))(\sqrt{3}) = \{c + d\sqrt{3}; c$ and d are in $Q(\sqrt{2})\}$. Is $(Q(\sqrt{2}))(\sqrt{3}) = Q(\sqrt{2}, \sqrt{3})$?

Suppose F is a field and x an indeterminate. By $F[x]$ we shall mean the set consisting of all expressions of the form $a_0 + a_1x + a_2x^2 + \cdots + a_nx^n$, where the elements a_i are in F and n is any nonnegative integer. Such an expression is called a *polynomial* in x over F. If we set $a_0 + a_1x + \cdots + a_nx^n = f(x)$, and $a_n \neq 0$, then the integer n is called the *degree* of the polynomial $f(x)$. (If $a_i = 0$ for all $i = 1, 2, \ldots, n$, we say the polynomial has degree 0.)

One can show that with "suitable" definitions for $+$ and $\cdot$ in the set $F[x]$, (for $f(x) = a_0 + a_1x + a_2x^2 + \cdots + a_nx^n$ and $g(x) = b_0 + b_1x + b_2x^2 + \cdots + b_mx^m$, let $f(x) + g(x) = c_0 + c_1x + c_2x^2 + \cdots + c_rx^r$ where $c_i = a_i + b_i$, and let $f(x) \cdot g(x) = d_0 + d_1x + d_2x^2 + \cdots + d_sx^s$ where $d_i = a_id_0 + a_{i-1}d_1 + \cdots + a_0d_i$), that all properties except property (8) of Definition 38 are satisfield. Thus it is to be remembered that $F[x]$ is *not* a field. (We remark here that if a set S is such that properties (1)-(4), (6), and (9) of Definition 38, together with the fact that $(b + c)a = ba + ca$ for all a, b, and c in S hold, then S is called a *ring*. Hence $F[x]$ is a ring. In fact, we can discuss $S[x]$ when S is not a field, but a ring, and still $S[x]$ will be a ring.)

As a generalization of the above, suppose F is a field with x_1 and x_2 indeterminates. We can construct $(F[x_1])[x_2]$ which is the set (ring) of the polynomials $b_0 + b_1x_2 + \cdots + b_mx_2^m$ where the b_i are in $F[x_1]$. That is, each b_i above is an expression of the form $a_0 + a_1x_1 + \cdots + a_nx_1^n$. A natural question to ask here would be: is $(F[x_1])[x_2]$ the same ring as the ring $(F[x_2])[x_1]$? Or more precisely, are these rings isomorphic? The answer is yes, and we denote these rings by $F[x_1, x_2]$. Generalizing further, we are led to the ring $F[x_1, x_2, \ldots, x_n]$ of polynomials in $x_1, x_2, \ldots, x_n$ over the field F.

In $F[x]$, if we form the set $F(x)$ of all quotients $\dfrac{f(x)}{g(x)}$, $g(x) \neq 0$, then with "suitable" definitions for $+$ and $\cdot$, $F(x)$ *is* a field; the field of quotients of $F[x]$. Generalizing, by $F(x_1, x_2, \ldots, x_n)$ we shall mean the field of quotients of $F[x_1, x_2, \ldots, x_n]$. $F(x_1, x_2, \ldots, x_n)$ is called the field of rational functions in $x_1, x_2, \ldots, x_n$ over F.

5-2. VECTOR SPACES

At this time we pause to give a brief discussion of vector spaces.

Definition 41 Let F be a field with respect to $+$ and $\cdot$ and suppose V is a nonempty set having defined on its elements a binary operation $*$. We call V a *vector space* over the field F if

1. V is an Abelian group with respect to $*$.
2. For a in F and x in V, there is an element which we denote by ax and ax is in V.
3. For all a and b in F and for all x and y in V, we have $a(x*y) = ax *ay$, $(a + b)x = ax * bx, a(bx) = (a \cdot b)x$, and $1x = x$. (1 is the unity of F.)

Note: The elements of V are usually called *vectors* and the elements of F are called *scalars*.

Example 43   Suppose R is the field of real numbers and let $V = \{(a_1, a_2, a_3);$ a_i is in $R\}$. We say that $(a_1, a_2, a_3) = (b_1, b_2, b_3)$ if $a_i = b_i$ for each i. We define $*$ on V as follows: $(a_1, a_2, a_3) * (b_1, b_2, b_3) = (a_1 + b_1, a_2 + b_2, a_3 + b_3)$ where the " $+$ " is ordinary addition for real numbers. If a is in R and $x = (a_1, a_2, a_3)$ is in V, we define ax to be $(a \cdot a_1, a \cdot a_2, a \cdot a_3)$ where the " $\cdot$ " is ordinary multiplication of real numbers. Note that ax is an element of V. V is a vector space over R.

Exercise 72   Show that if F is a field, then $F[x]$ may be regarded as a vector space over F.

Definition 42   Suppose V is a vector space over the field F and let $x_1, x_2, \ldots,$ x_n be elements of V. Any element of the form $a_1 x_1 + a_2 x_2 + \cdots + a_n x_n$, where the a_i are in F is called a *linear combination* of the x_i. (We are using $+$ in place of $*$.)

   The elements $x_1, x_2, \ldots, x_n$ are said to be *linearly dependent* if there exist elements $a_1, a_2, \ldots, a_n$ in F, not all 0, such that $a_1 x_1 + a_2 x_2 + \cdots + a_n x_n$ is equal to the identity element of V. If the elements $x_1, x_2, \ldots, x_n$ are not linearly dependent we shall say that they are *linearly independent*.

Definition 43   A subset S of the vector space V is called a *basis* of V if the elements of S are linearly independent and every element of V can be written as a linear combination of the elements in S.

Definition 44   A vector space V is said to be *finite-dimensional* if it has a basis S with a finite number of elements.

Remark 36   If V is a finite-dimensional vector space, then all bases of V have the same number of elements. The number of elements in a basis is called the *dimension* of V (over the field F).

Example 44   For the vector space of Example 43, the elements $x_1 = (1,1,2)$, $x_2 = (1,2,1)$, and $x_3 = (3,4,1)$ form a basis. That x_1, x_2, and x_3 are linearly independent is as follows: Suppose a_1, a_2, and a_3 belong to R and consider $a_1x_1 + a_2x_2 + a_3x_3$. Now if $a_1x_1 + a_2x_2 + a_3x_3$ is equal to the identity element of V (which is the element $(0,0,0)$) then we must have $(a_1, a_1, 2a_1) + (a_2, 2a_2, a_2) + (3a_3, 4a_3, a_3) = (0,0,0)$. This leads to the system of equations

$$a_1 + a_2 + 3a_3 = 0$$
$$a_1 + 2a_2 + 4a_3 = 0$$
$$2a_1 + a_2 + a_3 = 0$$

which has $a_1 = a_2 = a_3 = 0$ for its only solution.

Also, every element in V can be written as a linear combination of the elements x_1, x_2, and x_3. For suppose $x = (b_1, b_2, b_3)$ belongs to V. We must find elements a_1, a_2, and a_3 in R such that $a_1x_1 + a_2x_2 + a_3x_3 = x$, or such that $(a_1, a_1, 2a_1) + (a_2, 2a_2, a_2) + (3a_3, 4a_3, a_3) = (b_1, b_2, b_3)$. That a_1, a_2, and a_3 do exist follows by solving the system of equations

$$a_1 + a_2 + 3a_3 = b_1$$
$$a_1 + 2a_2 + 4a_3 = b_2$$
$$2a_1 + a_2 + a_3 = b_3$$

The elements $y_1 = (1,0,0)$, $y_2 = (0,1,0)$, and $y_3 = (0,0,1)$ also form a basis for V. The dimension of V (over R) is 3.

5-3. SPLITTING FIELDS

Returning now to our discussion of fields, it is clear that if K is an extension field of F, then we may regard K as a vector space over F. By the *degree* of K over F, we shall mean the dimension of K as a vector space over the field F. We denote the degree of K over F by $[K{:}F]$. If $[K{:}F]$ is finite (that is, if K has a basis with a finite number of elements) then we call K a finite extension of F.

Exercise 73 Find $[C{:}R]$, $[C{:}Q]$, $[R{:}Q]$, $[Q(\sqrt{2}){:}Q]$, $[(Q(\sqrt{2}))(\sqrt{3}){:}Q(\sqrt{2})]$, and $[(Q(\sqrt{2}))(\sqrt{3}){:}Q]$.

After working with Exercise 73, the reader has perhaps guessed the content of the following theorem.

Theorem 61 If K is a finite extension of E and E is a finite extension of F, then K is a finite extension of F and we have $[K{:}F] = [K{:}E][E{:}F]$.

Proof: We shall give an outline of the proof; details are left to the reader. Let $\{x_1, \ldots, x_n\}$ be a basis for K over E and $\{y_1, \ldots, y_m\}$ a basis for E over F. The elements x_iy_j ($i = 1, \ldots, n, j = 1, \ldots, m$) are linearly independent over F, and every element in K is a linear combination of these elements. Thus the nm elements x_iy_j form a basis for K over F.

Definition 45   Suppose K is an extension field of F and $f(x)$ is an element of $F[x]$. Let b belong to K. b is called a *root* of $f(x)$ if $f(b) = 0$. (If $f(x) = a_0 + a_1 x + \cdots + a_n x^n$, then $f(b) = a_0 + a_1 b + \cdots + a_n b^n$.)

The reader is surely familiar with the following theorem from elementary algebra, known as the *Factor theorem*.

Theorem 62   If b in K is a root of $f(x)$, where $f(x)$ is in $F[x]$, then $x - b$ divides (is a factor of) $f(x)$. (The converse also holds.)

Note: If b is a root of $f(x)$ then $x - b$ divides $f(x)$. Suppose $(x - b)^m$ divides $f(x)$, but $(x - b)^{m+1}$ does not. Then we say that b is a root of $f(x)$ having *multiplicity m*.

The polynomial $f(x) = x^3 + 2$ belongs to $Q[x]$, but no root of $f(x)$ belongs to Q. However, there are extensions of Q that contain at least one root of $f(x)$. In fact, there is an extension of Q containing all roots of $f(x)$. In general, if $f(x)$ belongs to $F[x]$, one can find an extension field of F containing *a* root of $f(x)$, and one can find an extension field of F containing *all* roots of $f(x)$. This will now be shown. First, we define what is meant by an irreducible polynomial over a field F.

Definition 46   Let $f(x)$ be an element of $F[x]$ and suppose we may write $f(x) = g(x)h(x)$ where $g(x)$ and $h(x)$ also are in $F[x]$. If this factorization of $f(x)$ is only possible when either $g(x)$ or $h(x)$ has degree 0, then we say that $f(x)$ is an *irreducible polynomial* over the field F.

Example 45 $f(x) = x^2 + 1$ is irreducible over R, the field of real numbers, but not over the field C of complex numbers, since in $C[x]$ we may write $f(x) = (x + i)(x - i)$. The polynomial $f(x) = x^3 + 2$ is irreducible over the field Q of rational numbers, but not over the field R, since in $R[x]$ we have $(x^3 + 2) = (x + \sqrt[3]{2})(x^2 - \sqrt[3]{2}x + \sqrt[3]{4})$. Here, $\sqrt[3]{2}$ denotes the real cube root of 2.

Theorem 63   Suppose $f(x)$ is an irreducible polynomial of degree $n \neq 0$ in $F[x]$. There is an extension field K of F such that
  1. $f(x)$ has a root in K, and
  2. $[K:F] = n$.

We omit the proof of this theorem, but shall prove the following:

Theorem 64   Suppose $f(x)$ is in $F[x]$ where the degree of $f(x)$ is $n \neq 0$. There is an extension K of F containing a root of $f(x)$.

Proof: This is immediate from Theorem 63. In fact, this *is* Theorem 63 if $f(x)$ is irreducible. If $f(x)$ is not irreducible over F, then we have $f(x) = g(x)h(x)$, where we may assume that $g(x)$ is irreducible (why?). Now by (1) of Theorem 63, $g(x)$ has a root in K. But then so does $f(x)$. Why?

Exercise 74 In Theorem 64 show that the degree of K over F must be less than, or equal to, the degree of $f(x)$.

Theorem 65 Suppose $f(x)$ is a polynomial of degree $n \neq 0$ in $F[x]$. There is an extension K of F such that $f(x)$ has n roots in K. (A root of multiplicity m is counted as m roots.) Furthermore, $[K:F] \leqslant n!$.

Proof: There is an extension K_1 of F such that $f(x)$ has a root b_1 in K_1 (Theorem 64), and $[K_1:F] \leqslant n$ (Exercise 74). Thus we may write $f(x) = (x - b_1)h_1(x)$ in $K_1[x]$, where $h_1(x)$ has degree $n - 1$. There is an extension K_2 of K_1 such that $h_1(x)$ (and hence $f(x)$) has a root b_2 in K_2 and $[K_2:K_1] \leqslant n - 1$. We may write $h_1(x) = (x - b_2)h_2(x)$ in $K_2[x]$, where $h_2(x)$ has degree $n - 2$. It follows that $f(x) = (x - b_1)(x - b_2)h_2(x)$. By a continuation of the above, we reach an extension field K_{n-1} of K_{n-2} such that $f(x)$ has a root b_{n-1} in K_{n-1} and $[K_{n-1}:K_{n-2}] \leqslant 2$. In $K_{n-1}[x]$ we have $f(x) = (x - b_1)(x - b_2) \cdots (x - b_{n-1})h_{n-1}(x)$. Clearly, $h_{n-1}(x) = x - a$, and so a is a root of $f(x)$. Thus if we set $K = K_{n-1}$, then $f(x)$ has n roots in K, and $[K:F] = [K_{n-1}:K_{n-2}][K_{n-2}:K_{n-3}] \cdots [K_1:F] \leqslant 2 \cdot 3 \cdots n = n!$.

Note: The reader may be wondering whether or not a polynomial $f(x)$ of degree n in $F[x]$ can have more than n roots in some extension field of F. This is not possible, as one can show by induction on the number n.

Reviewing the results just mentioned, if $f(x)$ is a polynomial of degree n over the field F, there is a finite extension K of F such that K contains the n roots $b_1, b_2, \ldots, b_n$ of $f(x)$. Now by Theorem 62, we may write $f(x) = (x - b_1)(x - b_2) \cdots (x - b_n)$ in $K[x]$. That is, in $K[x]$, the polynomial $f(x)$ splits (factors) into a product of factors each having degree 1. (Such a factor is called *linear*.)

It is clear that there exists an extension K of F such that $f(x)$ splits into linear factors over K and $[K:F]$ is minimal.

Definition 47 Let $f(x)$ be an element of $F[x]$. A finite extension K of F is called a *splitting field* over F of $f(x)$ if $f(x)$ can be written as a product of linear factors in $K[x]$ and $[K:F]$ is minimal. (That is, $f(x)$ splits into linear factors over K, but does not split into linear factors over any subfield of K.)

Note: K is a splitting field over F of $f(x)$, where $f(x)$ has degree n, if K is a finite extension having minimal degree over F and such that K contains n roots of $f(x)$.

Example 46 Consider again the polynomial $f(x) = x^3 + 2$ in $Q[x]$. Now $Q(-\sqrt[3]{2})$ is an extension of Q containing a root of $f(x)$, but $Q(-\sqrt[3]{2})$ is not a splitting field over Q of $f(x)$. The factorization of $f(x)$ in $(Q(-\sqrt[3]{2}))[x]$ is $(x + \sqrt[3]{2})(x^2 - \sqrt[3]{2}x + \sqrt[3]{4})$, where clearly, $x^2 - \sqrt[3]{2}x + \sqrt[3]{4}$ is irreducible over

$Q(-\sqrt[3]{2})$. Now by Theorem 65, a splitting field K over Q of $x^3 + 2$ is such that $[K:Q] \leqslant 6$. Since $[Q(-\sqrt[3]{2}):Q] = 3$ (the reader should show this by exhibiting a basis consisting of 3 elements for $Q(-\sqrt[3]{2})$ over Q), it follows that K must be an extension field of $Q(-\sqrt[3]{2})$ having degree 2 over $Q(-\sqrt[3]{2})$ and containing the roots of the polynomial $x^2 - \sqrt[3]{2}x + \sqrt[3]{4}$. Such an extension is $(Q(-\sqrt[3]{2}))(i\sqrt{3})$. (To see this, solve $x^2 - \sqrt[3]{2}x + \sqrt[3]{4}$ by the quadratic formula.) Therefore, a splitting field of $x^3 + 2$ over Q is $K = Q(-\sqrt[3]{2}, i\sqrt{3})$.

Exercise 75   Find a basis for $Q(-\sqrt[3]{2}, i\sqrt{3})$ over Q.

Remark 37   In Example 46 we found a splitting field of $x^3 + 2$. One should wonder if a polynomial $f(x)$ can have more than one splitting field over the field F. Essentially the answer is no, since it can be shown that if K_1 and K_2 are two splitting fields for the polynomial $f(x)$ over the field F, then K_1 and K_2 are isomorphic. In fact, there is an isomorphism π from K_1 onto K_2 such that $\pi(x) = x$ for all x in F. (By an isomorphism of a field F onto a field F' we mean a 1-1 mapping π from F onto F' such that $\pi(x + y) = \pi(x) + \pi(y)$ and $\pi(xy) = \pi(x)\pi(y)$ for all x and y in F.)

5-4.   THE GALOIS GROUP OF A POLYNOMIAL
FUNDAMENTAL THEOREM OF GALOIS THEORY

Now that some of the necessary background in field theory has been discussed, we are ready to return to a discussion of groups and their relationship to the roots of a polynomial over a field. In what follows, we assume that all fields are of characteristic O. That is, if n is an integer and $a \neq 0$ belongs to the field, $na = 0$ implies $n = 0$.

Definition 48   Suppose K is a field and α is a 1-1 mapping from K onto itself such that $\alpha(x + y) = \alpha(x) + \alpha(y)$ and $\alpha(xy) = \alpha(x)\alpha(y)$ for all x and y in K. We call α an *automorphism* of K.

Note: An automorphism of K is an isomorphism of K onto itself.

Exercise 76   Prove that the automorphisms of a field K form a group (with respect to multiplication of mappings), which we denote by $A(K)$.

Remark 38   Suppose G is a group of automorphisms of the field K (G is *not* necessarily all of $A(K)$), and let $K_G = \{x$ in $K; \alpha(x) = x$ for all α in $G\}$. K_G is a subfield of K, which we shall call the *fixed field of* G.

Proof: Let x and y be elements of K_G. Then for all α in G we have $\alpha(x) = x$ and $\alpha(y) = y$. Now $\alpha(x + y) = \alpha(x) + \alpha(y) = x + y$ and $\alpha(xy) = \alpha(x)\alpha(y) = xy$.

Thus $x + y$ and xy are in K_G. Since $\alpha(-x) = -\alpha(x) = -x$, $-x$ belongs to K_G. Let $x \neq 0$ be an element of K_G. Then $\alpha(x^{-1}) = \alpha(x)^{-1} = x^{-1}$, and x^{-1} is in K_G. Therefore K_G is a subfield of K (Remark 34).

If K is an extension field of the field F, we shall denote by $A(K,F)$ the set of automorphisms of K that leave every element of F fixed. That is, $A(K,F) = \{\alpha$ in $A(K); \alpha(x) = x$ for all x in $F\}$.

Theorem 66 $A(K,F)$ is a subgroup of the group $A(K)$.

Proof: Clearly, $A(K,F)$ is a nonempty subset of $A(K)$. (Why?) Let α_1 and α_2 belong to $A(K,F)$ and suppose x is in F. Since $(\alpha_1\alpha_2)(x) = \alpha_1(\alpha_2(x)) = \alpha_1(x) = x$, $\alpha_1\alpha_2$ belongs to $A(K,F)$. Since $\alpha(x) = x$ implies that $\alpha^{-1}(\alpha(x)) = \alpha^{-1}(x)$, or that $x = \alpha^{-1}(x)$, α^{-1} is in $A(K,F)$. Thus, $A(K,F)$ is a subgroup of $A(K)$ by Theorem 5.

Note: $F \subseteq K_{A(K,F)}$.

The groups $A(K,F)$ are of such importance that we emphasize them with several examples.

Example 47 If R is the field of real numbers and C is the field of complex numbers, then we have $|A(C,R)| = 2$. For suppose α belongs to $A(C,R)$. Since $-1 = \alpha(-1) = \alpha(i^2) = [\alpha(i)]^2$, it must be the case that $\alpha(i)$ is i or $-i$. Now α leaves every element of R fixed. Therefore the two mappings α_1 and α_2 defined by $\alpha_1(a + bi) = a + bi$ and $\alpha_2(a + bi) = a - bi$ are the only automorphisms in $A(C,R)$. If $a + bi$ belongs to $C_{A(C,R)}$, the fixed field of $A(C,R)$, then $\alpha(a + bi) = a + bi$ for all α in $A(C,R)$. In particular, we have $\alpha_2(a + bi) = a + bi$, which implies that $a + bi = a - bi$ or that $b = 0$. Therefore $C_{A(C,R)} = R$.

Example 48 Let us find $A(Q(-\sqrt[3]{2}, i\sqrt{3}), Q)$. We may take as a basis for $Q(-\sqrt[3]{2}, i\sqrt{3})$ over Q the set $\{1, -\sqrt[3]{2}, \sqrt[3]{4}, i\sqrt{3}, -i\sqrt{3}\,\sqrt[3]{2}, i\sqrt{3}\,\sqrt[3]{4}\}$. (See Example 46 and Exercise 75.) The automorphisms of $Q(-\sqrt[3]{2}, i\sqrt{3})$ will be determined by the images of these basis elements; or particularly by the images of the elements $-\sqrt[3]{2}$ and $i\sqrt{3}$. Let α belong to $A(Q(-\sqrt[3]{2}, i\sqrt{3}), Q)$. Since $[\alpha(-\sqrt[3]{2})]^3 = \alpha((-\sqrt[3]{2})^3) = \alpha(-2) = -2$, $\alpha(-\sqrt[3]{2})$ must be a cube root of -2. Thus the possible images for $-\sqrt[3]{2}$ are $-\sqrt[3]{2}, \sqrt[3]{2}\left(\dfrac{1 + i\sqrt{3}}{2}\right)$, and $\sqrt[3]{2}\left(\dfrac{1 - i\sqrt{3}}{2}\right)$.

Since $[\alpha(i\sqrt{3})]^2 = \alpha((i\sqrt{3})^2) = \alpha(-3) = -3$, $\alpha(i\sqrt{3})$ must be a square root of -3. Thus the possible images for $i\sqrt{3}$ are $i\sqrt{3}$ and $-i\sqrt{3}$. It follows that there are 6 automorphisms of $Q(-\sqrt[3]{2}, i\sqrt{3})$. These are denoted by $\alpha_1, \alpha_2, \alpha_3, \alpha_4, \alpha_5$, and α_6, where

$$\alpha_1(-\sqrt[3]{2}) = -\sqrt[3]{2},$$

$$\alpha_2(-\sqrt[3]{2}) = -\sqrt[3]{2},$$

$$\alpha_3(-\sqrt[3]{2}) = \sqrt[3]{2}\left(\frac{1 + i\sqrt{3}}{2}\right),$$

$$\alpha_4(-\sqrt[3]{2}) = \sqrt[3]{2}\left(\frac{1 - i\sqrt{3}}{2}\right),$$

$$\alpha_5(-\sqrt[3]{2}) = \sqrt[3]{2}\left(\frac{1 - i\sqrt{3}}{2}\right),$$

$$\alpha_6(-\sqrt[3]{2}) = \sqrt[3]{2}\left(\frac{1 - i\sqrt{3}}{2}\right),$$

$$\alpha_1(i\sqrt{3}) = i\sqrt{3}$$

$$\alpha_2(i\sqrt{3}) = -i\sqrt{3}$$

$$\alpha_3(i\sqrt{3}) = i\sqrt{3}$$

$$\alpha_4(i\sqrt{3}) = -i\sqrt{3}$$

$$\alpha_5(i\sqrt{3}) = i\sqrt{3}$$

$$\alpha_6(i\sqrt{3}) = -i\sqrt{3}$$

Table 23 is the group table for $A(Q(-\sqrt[3]{2}, i\sqrt{3}), Q)$.

TABLE 23

	α_1	α_2	α_3	α_4	α_5	α_6
α_1	α_1	α_2	α_3	α_4	α_5	α_6
α_2	α_2	α_1	α_6	α_5	α_4	α_3
α_3	α_3	α_4	α_5	α_6	α_1	α_2
α_4	α_4	α_3	α_2	α_1	α_6	α_5
α_5	α_5	α_6	α_1	α_2	α_3	α_4
α_6	α_6	α_5	α_4	α_3	α_2	α_1

Exercise 77   Show that $A(Q(-\sqrt[3]{2}, i\sqrt{3}), Q)$ is isomorphic to the group of Table 13 (and hence is also isomorphic to S_3 by Exercise 61).

Exercise 78   Suppose K is an extension of Q, the field of rationals. Show that any automorphism α of K must leave every element of Q fixed. [*Hint:* start with the fact that $\alpha(1) = 1$.]

Example 49   For the group $A(Q(\sqrt[3]{5}), Q)$, we must have $\alpha(\sqrt[3]{5}) = \sqrt[3]{5}$ for any automorphism α since there is only one cube root of 5 in $Q(\sqrt[3]{5})$. Since every element in $Q(\sqrt[3]{5})$ is of the form $a + b\sqrt[3]{5} + c\sqrt[3]{25}$ where a, b, and c are in Q, we have that $\alpha(a + b\sqrt[3]{5} + c\sqrt[3]{25}) = \alpha(a) + \alpha(b)\alpha(\sqrt[3]{5}) + \alpha(c)\alpha(\sqrt[3]{25}) = a + b\sqrt[3]{5} + c\sqrt[3]{25}$. Therefore there is only one automorphism in $A(Q(\sqrt[3]{5}), Q)$; namely the identity map. Here, the fixed field of $A(Q(\sqrt[3]{5}), Q)$ is $Q(\sqrt[3]{5})$.

Remark 39   One has perhaps observed from the previous examples that the order of $A(K, F)$ has been less than, or equal to, the degree of K over F. It is true that whenever K is a finite extension of F, then $|A(K,F)| \leq [K:F]$. Equality holds when K is an extension of a particular type, called a normal extension. Such an extension is now defined.

Definition 49 Suppose K is a finite extension of F. If there is an α in $A(K,F)$ such that $\alpha(x) \neq x$ where x belongs to K, (but not to F), then K is said to be a *normal extension* of F.

Note: K is a normal extension of F if the fixed field $K_{A(K,F)}$ of $A(K,F)$ is F.

The normal extensions K of a field F are characterized by the following theorem.

Theorem 67 K is a normal extension of F if, and only if, K is the splitting field of some polynomial $f(x)$ in $F[x]$.

At this time we shall define what is meant by the Galois group of a polynomial $f(x)$ over F and discuss the important theorem known as the fundamental theorem of Galois theory. This theorem will establish a 1-1 correspondence between the subfields of the splitting field of $f(x)$ that contain F and subgroups of the Galois group of $f(x)$.

Definition 50   Let $f(x)$ be an element of $F[x]$ and suppose K is its splitting field over F. The *Galois group* of $f(x)$ is the group $A(K,F)$.

Note: Henceforth, we shall use the notation $G(K,F)$ to denote the Galois group of $f(x)$. We also note that $G(K,F)$ may be regarded as a group of permutations of the roots of $f(x)$, since roots of $f(x)$ are mapped onto roots of $f(x)$ by automorphisms in $G(K,F)$.

Theorem 68   Suppose $f(x)$ belongs to $F[x]$ and K is the splitting field of $f(x)$. Let S denote the collection of subfields E of K such that $F \subseteq E$ and let S' be the collection of subgroups of $G(K,F)$. The mapping $g:S \rightarrow S'$ defined by $g(E) = G(K,E)$ is a 1-1 mapping from S onto S'. Furthermore, we have

1. $E = K_{G(K,E)}$.
2. If H is a subgroup of $G(K,F)$, then $H = G(K,K_H)$.
3. $[K:E] = |G(K,E)|$; $[E:F] = |G(K,F)/G(K,E)|$.
4. E is a normal extension of F if, and only if, $G(K,E)$ is a normal subgroup of $G(K,F)$.
5. If E is a normal extension of F, then $G(E,F)$ is isomorphic to the quotient group $G(K,F)/G(K,E)$.

Proof: K is the splitting field over E of $f(x)$ since it is the splitting field over F of $f(x)$, and $F \subseteq E$. Thus K is a normal extension of E (Theorem 67) and we have E is the fixed field of $G(K,E)$. (See note following Definition 49.) Therefore $E = K_{G(K,E)}$.

Now suppose $g(E_1) = g(E_2)$. That is, suppose $G(K,E_1) = G(K,E_2)$. By what has just been proved, we have $E_1 = K_{G(K,E_1)} = K_{G(K,E_2)} = E_2$. This says that g is a 1-1 mapping.

We do not prove (2) of the theorem, but note that this implies that g is a mapping from S onto S'. For if H is a subgroup of $G(K,F)$ and $H = G(K,K_H)$, then K_H is a subfield of K containing F with $g(K_H) = G(K,K_H)$.

Since K is a normal extension of E we have $|G(K,E)| = [K:E]$ (Remark 39). Also, $|G(K,F)| = [K:F] = [K:E][E:F] = |G(K,E)| \cdot [E:F]$, which implies that the degree of E over F is the index of $G(K,E)$ in $G(K,F)$. This is (3).

Now E will be a normal extension of F if, and only if, whenever α belongs to $G(K,F)$ and x is in E, then $\alpha(x)$ is also in E. (We do not prove this fact here.) Thus, suppose α belongs to $G(K,F)$, α' belongs to $G(K,E)$, and x belongs to E. Then E is a normal extension of F if, and only if, $\alpha'(\alpha(x)) = \alpha(x)$; or if, and only if, $\alpha^{-1}[\alpha'(\alpha(x))] = (\alpha^{-1}\alpha'\alpha)(x) = x$. It follows that E is a normal extension of F if, and only if, $\alpha^{-1}\alpha'\alpha$ is in $G(K,E)$ for all α in $G(K,F)$ and for all α' in $G(K,E)$. Hence $G(K,E)$ is a normal subgroup of $G(K,F)$ by Remark 15.

It remains to show that (5) holds. If we can find a homomorphism φ from $G(K,F)$ onto $G(E,F)$ such that the kernel of φ is $G(K,E)$, then we have it. (See Theorem 22.) Let α belong to $G(K,F)$ and let $\varphi: G(K,F) \to G(E,F)$ be defined by $\varphi(\alpha) = \pi$, where π is the mapping defined by $\pi(x) = \alpha(x)$, x in E. We first note that φ is well defined. Since E is a normal extension of F, if α belongs to $G(K,F)$, then $\alpha(x)$ belongs to E whenever x is in E. Now if x is also in F then clearly, $\alpha(x) = x$ (since α is in $G(K,F)$), and so π *is* an element of $G(E,F)$. It is left to the reader to show φ is actually a homomorphism.

Now suppose α is in $G(K,F)$ and $\varphi(\alpha)$ is the identity map of $G(E,F)$. Then it must be the case that $\alpha(x) = x$ for all x in E. Thus α belongs to $G(K,E)$. Clearly, if α belongs to $G(K,E)$, then $\varphi(\alpha)$ is the identity map of $G(E,F)$. Therefore $G(K,E)$ is the kernel of φ.

Finally, the image under φ of $G(K,F)$ in $G(E,F)$ is isomorphic to the quotient group $G(K,F)/G(K,E)$. (Theorem 22 applies. How?) Now $|G(K,F)/G(K,E)| = [E:F]$ (why?) $= |G(E,F)|$. This implies that φ must be onto.

We now illustrate the fundamental theorem of Galois theory with the following example.

Example 50 The Galois group of $x^3 + 2$ is the group $A(Q(-\sqrt[3]{2}, i\sqrt{3}), Q)$ defined by Table 23. (See Examples 46 and 48.) Now the subgroups of the Galois group are: $\{\alpha_1\}$, $H_1 = \{\alpha_1, \alpha_2\}$, $H_2 = \{\alpha_1, \alpha_4\}$, $H_3 = \{\alpha_1, \alpha_6\}$, $H_4 = \{\alpha_1, \alpha_3, \alpha_5\}$, and $\{\alpha_1, \alpha_2, \alpha_3, \alpha_4, \alpha_5, \alpha_6\}$. These subgroups are in 1-1 correspondence with the subfields of $Q(-\sqrt[3]{2}, i\sqrt{3})$ that contain Q as indicated by

$$\{e\} \longleftrightarrow Q(-\sqrt[3]{2}, i\sqrt{3})$$

$$H_1 \longleftrightarrow Q(-\sqrt[3]{2})$$

$$H_2 \longleftrightarrow Q\left(\sqrt[3]{2} \, \frac{1 - i\sqrt{3}}{2}\right)$$

$$H_3 \longleftrightarrow Q\left(\sqrt[3]{2} \, \frac{1 + i\sqrt{3}}{2}\right)$$

$$H_4 \longleftrightarrow Q(i\sqrt{3})$$

$$\{\alpha_1, \alpha_2, \alpha_3, \alpha_4, \alpha_5, \alpha_6\} \longleftrightarrow Q$$

Since H_4 is normal in $\{\alpha_1, \alpha_2, \alpha_3, \alpha_4, \alpha_5, \alpha_6\}$ (why?) we have $Q(i\sqrt{3})$ is a normal extension of Q. Thus $Q(i\sqrt{3})$ is the splitting field of some polynomial $f(x)$ in $F[x]$ by Theorem 67. (Which polynomial?) Are any of the remaining fields $Q\left(\sqrt[3]{2}\left(\frac{1 + i\sqrt{3}}{2}\right)\right)$, $Q\left(\sqrt[3]{2}\left(\frac{1 - i\sqrt{3}}{2}\right)\right)$, or $Q(-\sqrt[3]{2})$ normal extensions of Q?

Since $Q(i\sqrt{3})$ is a normal extension of Q, then $G(Q(i\sqrt{3}),Q)$ is isomorphic to the quotient group $G(Q(-\sqrt[3]{2}, i\sqrt{3}), Q)/G(Q(-\sqrt[3]{2}, i\sqrt{3}), Q(i\sqrt{3}))$. The reader should find the two cosets of this quotient group, and the two automorphisms in $G(Q(i\sqrt{3}),Q)$ and establish the isomorphism.

5-5. SOLVABILITY BY RADICALS

We are about ready to show that if the general nth degree equation is solvable by radicals, then the symmetric group S_n is a solvable group. (The converse of this is also true, but we shall omit the proof.) Our approach is founded on the treatment given by I. N. Herstein in his *Topics in Algebra* (New York: Blaisdell, 1964).

First, we state what is meant by saying that the polynomial $f(x)$ of $F[x]$ is solvable by radicals over the field F. (The reader should recall Remark 35.)

Definition 51 Suppose F is a field and $f(x)$ is a polynomial belonging to $F[x]$. We say that $f(x)$ is *solvable by radicals over* F if there exist fields $F_1, F_2, \ldots, F_r$ such that

1. $F_i = F_{i-1}(b_i)$, where b_i is a root of the polynomial $x^{n_i} - a_i$ in $F_{i-1}[x]$, (here, $F_0 = F$) and
2. all roots of $f(x)$ are in F_r.

Remark 40   If b_i is a root of $x^{n_i} - a_i$, then b_i is an nth root of a_i. Also, if K is the splitting field of $f(x)$ over F and $f(x)$ is solvable by radicals (over F), then $K \subset F_r$.

Example 51   Consider the polynomial $f(x) = x^2 + 2x - 4$ in $Q[x]$, Q the field of rationals. Now the roots of $f(x)$ are $-1 \pm \sqrt{5}$. Letting $Q_1 = Q_0(b_1)$, where $Q_0 = Q$ and $b_1 = \sqrt{5}$, we see that $f(x)$ is solvable by radicals over Q. ($F_r = Q_1$ and $x^{n_i} - a_i = x^2 - 5$.)

By the *general* polynomial of degree n over the field F we have meant the polynomial $f(x) = x^n - a_1 x^{n-1} + a_2 x^{n-2} - + \cdots + (-1)^n a_n$ where the a_i are in F. We note that $f(x)$ may be regarded as a *particular* polynomial over $F(a_1, a_2, \ldots, a_n)$, the field of rational functions in $a_1, a_2, \ldots, a_n$ over F. (See last paragraph of Sec. 5-1.) To say that $f(x)$ is solvable by radicals shall mean that it is solvable by radicals over the field $F(a_1, a_2, \ldots, a_n)$.

Remark 41   One can show that if F is a field containing the nth roots of unity for a particular choice of n, then the splitting field K of $x^n - a$ ($a \neq 0$ in F) is the field $F(b)$ where b is *any* root of $x^n - a$. It is also true that the Galois group of $x^n - a$ is an Abelian group. We give a proof of this.

Proof: Let α_1 and α_2 belong to the Galois group of $x^n - a$. Then α_1 and α_2 are automorphisms of K (where $K = F(b)$) that leave every element in F fixed. (See Definition 50.) Now $\alpha_1(b)$ and $\alpha_2(b)$ are roots of $x^n - a$ (why?) and so we have $\alpha_1(b) = \omega^i b$ and $\alpha_2(b) = \omega^j b$ for some i and j such that $1 \leq i \leq n - 1$, $1 \leq j \leq n - 1$. (ω is an nth root of unity. Remember that F contains all the nth roots of unity for our choice of n.) It follows that $(\alpha_1 \alpha_2)(b) = \alpha_1 \cdot (\alpha_2(b)) = \alpha_1(\omega^j b) = \omega^j \alpha_1(b) = \omega^j \omega^i b = \omega^{j+i} b$, and that $(\alpha_2 \alpha_1)(b) = \alpha_2 (\alpha_1 \cdot (b)) = \alpha_2(\omega^i b) = \omega^i \alpha_2(b) = \omega^i \omega^j b = \omega^{i+j} b$. Thus $\alpha_1 \alpha_2$ and $\alpha_2 \alpha_1$ have the same effect on b. But since they have the same effect on any x in F, they have the same effect on the elements of $F(b) = K$. Therefore, $\alpha_1 \alpha_2 = \alpha_2 \alpha_1$ and the Galois group is Abelian.

Theorem 69   Suppose F is a field containing the nth roots of unity for *any* choice of n. Also suppose that $f(x)$ in $F[x]$ is solvable by radicals over F. Then the Galois group of $f(x)$ is a solvable group. (The reader should review the last part of Sec. 2–3, beginning with Definition 31.)

Proof: Let K be the splitting field of $f(x)$. Since $f(x)$ is solvable by radicals over F, there exist fields $F_1, F_2, \ldots, F_r$ such that $F_i = F_{i-1}(b_i)$ where b_i is a root of $x^{n_i} - a_i$, a polynomial in $F_{i-1}[x]$, and such that all roots of $f(x)$ are in F (Definition 51). Now we may assume that F_r is a normal extension of F. (Try to prove this!) Thus F_r is a normal extension of each field F_i (Theorem 67). Since F_i is normal over F_{i-1} (Remark 41), $G(F_r, F_i)$ is a normal subgroup of $G(F_r,F_{i-1})$. (By Theorem 68.) Therefore, the series $\{e\} \subset G(F_r, F_{r-1}) \subset G(F_r,F_{r-2}) \subset \cdots \subset G(F_r,F_1) \subset G(F_r,F)$ is a normal series. Again by Theorem 68, we have $G(F_i,F_{i-1})$ is isomorphic to $G(F_r,F_{i-1})/G(F_r,F_i)$. But $G(F_i,F_{i-1})$ is Abelian (Remark 41). Therefore each factor of the above normal series is Abelian, which implies that $G(F_r,F)$ is a solvable group (Theorem 36). (Remember that we are trying to show that $G(K,F)$ is solvable!)

Now $K \subset F_r$ (Remark 40) and K is normal over F (why?). Thus, from Theorem 68 (again!), $G(F_r,K)$ is normal in $G(F_r,F)$ and $G(K,F)$ is isomorphic to $G(F_r,F)/G(F_r,K)$. Since $G(F_r,F)/G(F_r,K)$ is a solvable group (Exercise 40), it follows that $G(K,F)$ is also solvable.

Note: Theorem 69 is true even when F does *not* contain roots of unity.

The end is finally in sight. If we recall what our goal is, and what is meant by saying that the general nth degree equation $f(x)$ is solvable by radicals (comment following Example 51), all that remains to be shown is that the Galois group of $f(x)$ over $F(a_1,a_2,\ldots,a_n)$ is S_n. This is the famous theorem due to Abel.

Let α belong to S_n. The mapping $\alpha : F(x_1,x_2,\ldots,x_n) \to F(x_1,x_2,\ldots,x_n)$ defined by $\alpha(r(x_1,x_2,\ldots,x_n)) = r(x_{\alpha(1)},x_{\alpha(2)},\ldots,x_{\alpha(n)})$ is an automorphism of $F(x_1,x_2,\ldots,x_n)$. Now the fixed field $F(x_1,x_2,\ldots,x_n)_{S_n}$ of S_n is the set of all elements $r(x_1,x_2,\ldots,x_n)$ in $F(x_1,x_2,\ldots,x_n)$ such that $\alpha(r(x_1,x_2,\ldots,x_n)) = r(x_1,x_2,\ldots,x_n)$ for all α in S_n. (See Remark 38.) That is, all elements $r(x_1,x_2,\ldots,x_n)$ in $F(x_1,x_2,\ldots,x_n)$ such that $r(x_1,x_2,\ldots,x_n) = r(x_{\alpha(1)}, x_{\alpha(2)},\ldots,x_{\alpha(n)})$ for all α in S_n. (In what follows we let $S = F(x_1,x_2,\ldots,x_n)_{S_n}$.)

Next let $a_1 = x_1 + x_2 + \cdots + x_n$, $a_2 = x_1x_2 + x_1x_3 + \cdots + x_1x_n + x_2x_3 + x_2x_4 + \cdots + x_2x_n + \cdots + x_{n-1}x_n, \ldots$, $a_n = x_1x_2 \cdots x_n$, and consider $F(a_1,a_2, \ldots,a_n)$. $F(a_1,a_2,\ldots,a_n)$ is a subfield of S. (Prove that the a_i belong to S.) Clearly, S_n is a subgroup of $G(F(x_1,x_2,\ldots,x_n),S)$. By Remark 39, $|G(F(x_1, x_2,\ldots,x_n),S)| \leqslant [F(x_1,x_2,\ldots,x_n):S]$. Since $|S_n| \leqslant |G(F(x_1,x_2,\ldots,x_n), S)|$, it follows that $n! \leqslant [F(x_1,x_2,\ldots,x_n):S]$.

Now note that the general polynomial $f(x) = x^n - a_1x^{n-1} + a_2x^{n-2} - + \cdots + (-1)^n a_n$ belongs to $F(a_1,a_2,\ldots,a_n)[x]$ and that $f(x) = (x - x_1)(x - x_2) \cdots (x - x_n)$. (Remember what the a_i are.) It follows that $F(x_1,x_2,\ldots,x_n)$ is the splitting field of $f(x)$ over $F(a_1,a_2,\ldots,a_n)$ where $[F(x_1,x_2,\ldots,x_n):F(a_1,a_2,\ldots,a_n)] \leqslant n!$. (See Theorem 65 and Definition 47.)

Finally, since $F(a_1,a_2,\ldots,a_n) \subseteq S \subset F(x_1,x_2,\ldots,x_n)$, we have (from what has already been shown above) that $n! \leqslant [F(x_1,x_2,\ldots,x_n):S][S:F(a_1, a_2,\ldots,a_n)] = [F(x_1,x_2,\ldots,x_n):F(a_1,a_2,\ldots,a_n)] \leqslant n!$; which implies that $[S:F(a_1,a_2,\ldots,a_n)] = 1$. Therefore $S = F(a_1,a_2,\ldots,a_n)$, and $S_n = G(F(x_1, x_2,\ldots,x_n),F(a_1,a_2,\ldots,a_n))$. (This also follows by what was shown above.)

Final Remark In order for the general nth degree polynomial $f(x) = x^n - a_1x^{n-1} + a_2x^{n-2} - + \cdots + (-1)^n a_n$ to be solvable by radicals, the Galois group of $f(x)$ must be a solvable group (Theorem 69). We have just shown that the Galois group of $f(x)$ is S_n. Since S_n is not a solvable group for $n \geqslant 5$ (Remark 23), the general nth degree polynomial, where $n \geqslant 5$, is not solvable by radicals.

Index